Dear Reader

*This booklet "hotels and restaurants"
is an extract from the Michelin Guide
"GREAT BRITAIN and IRELAND" 1992
and has been created specially
for your visits to London.*

*The unbiased and independent selection
of hotels and restaurants
is the result of local visits and enquiries
by our inspectors.
In addition we receive considerable help
from our readers' invaluable letters
and comments.*

*It is our purpose
to provide up-to-date information
and thus render a service to our readers.
The next edition is already in preparation.*

*Therefore, only the guide of the year
merits your complete confidence,
so please remember to use the latest edition*

*For a detailed tour of the city,
use the Michelin Green Guide "LONDON".*

*We wish you a pleasant stay
in the British capital !*

Contents

Choosing
a hotel or restaurant

This guide offers a selection of hotels and restaurants to help the motorist on his travels. In each category establishments are listed in order of preference according to the degree of comfort they offer.

CATEGORIES

🏨	Luxury in the traditional style	XXXXX
🏨	Top class comfort	XXXX
🏨	Very comfortable	XXX
🏨	Comfortable	XX
🏠	Quite comfortable	X
🏠	Other recommended accommodation, at moderate prices	
without rest.	The hotel has no restaurant	
	The restaurant also offers accommodation	with rm

PEACEFUL ATMOSPHERE AND SETTING

Certain establishments are distinguished in the guide by the red symbols shown below.
Your stay in such hotels will be particularly pleasant or restful, owing to the character of the building, its decor, the setting, the welcome and services offered, or simply the peace and quiet to be enjoyed there.

🏨 to 🏠	Pleasant hotels
XXXXX to X	Pleasant restaurants
« Riverside setting »	Particularly attractive feature
🦢	Very quiet or quiet, secluded hotel
🦢	Quiet hotel
≤ London	Exceptional view
≤	Interesting or extensive view

1   V

Hotel facilities

In general the hotels we recommend have full bathroom and toilet facilities in each room. However, this may not be the case for certain rooms in categories 🏨, ▥, ✿ and ⌂.

30 rm	Number of rooms
⬍	Lift (elevator)
▤	Air conditioning
TV	Television in room
⇟	Establishment either partly or wholly reserved for non-smokers
🕾	Telephone in room: outside calls connected by the operator
☎	Telephone in room: direct dialling for outside calls
ঙ	Rooms accessible to disabled people
⚲ ▨	Outdoor or indoor swimming pool
🏋 ⌖	Exercise room – Sauna
🎋	Garden
✗ ⌐₉	Hotel tennis court – Golf course and number of holes
♨ 150	Equipped conference hall: maximum capacity
🚗	Hotel garage (additional charge in most cases)
Ⓟ	Car park for customers only
⚘	Dogs are not allowed in all or part of the hotel
Fax	Telephone document transmission
closed *Saturday* *and August*	Dates when closed as indicated by the restaurateur
LL35 OSB	Postal code
(Forte)	Hotel Group (See list on page XLII.)

Animals

It is forbidden to bring domestic animals (dogs, cats...) into Great Britain and Ireland.

Cuisine

STARS

Certain establishments deserve to be brought to your attention for the particularly fine quality of their cooking. **Michelin stars** are awarded for the standard of meals served.

For each of these restaurants we indicate three culinary specialities typical of their style of cooking to assist you in your choice.

✿✿✿	**Exceptional cuisine, worth a special journey** Superb food, fine wines, faultless service, elegant surroundings. One will pay accordingly !
✿✿	**Excellent cooking, worth a detour** Specialities and wines of first class quality. This will be reflected in the price.
✿	**A very good restaurant in its category** The star indicates a good place to stop on your journey. But beware of comparing the star given to an expensive « de luxe » establishment to that of a simple restaurant where you can appreciate fine cooking at a reasonable price.

THE RED « M »

Whilst appreciating the quality of the cooking in restaurants with a star, you may, however, wish to find some serving a perhaps less elaborate but nonetheless always carefully prepared meal.

Certain restaurants seem to us to answer this requirement. We bring them to your attention by marking them with a red « M » in the text of the Guide.

Alcoholic beverages-conditions of sale

The sale of alcoholic drinks is governed in Great Britain and Ireland by licensing laws which vary greatly from country to country.

Allowing for local variations, restaurants may stay open and serve alcohol with a bona fide meal during the afternoon. Hotel bars and public houses are generally open between 11am and 11pm at the discretion of the licensee. Hotel residents, however, may buy drinks outside the permitted hours at the discretion of the hotelier.

Children under the age of 14 are not allowed in bars.

Prices

Prices quoted are valid for autumn 1991. Changes may arise if goods and service costs are revised.

Your recommendation is self-evident if you always walk into a hotel guide in hand.

Hotels and restaurants in bold type have supplied details of all their rates and have assumed responsibility for maintaining them for all travellers in possession of this guide.

Prices are given in £ sterling.

Where no mentoin **s., t.,** or **st.** is shown, prices are subject to the addition of service charge, V.A.T., or both.

MEALS

M 13.00/24.00	**Set meals** – Lunch 13.00, dinner 24.00 – including cover charge, where applicable
M 15.00/25.00	See page 7
s.	Service only included
t.	V.A.T. only included
st.	Service and V.A.T. included
🍾 6.00	Price of 1/2 bottle or carafe of house wine
M a la carte 20.00/25.00	**A la carte meals** – The prices represent the range of charges from a simple to an elaborate 3 course meal and include a cover charge where applicable
☕ 8.50	Charge for full cooked breakfast (i.e. not included in the room rate) Continental breakfast may be available at a lower rate

⌂ : Dinner in this category of establishment will generally be offered from a fixed price menu of limited choice, served at a set time to residents only. Lunch is rarely offered. Many will not be licensed to sell alcohol.

ROOMS

rm 80.00/150.00	Lowest price 80.00 per room for a comfortable single and highest price 150.00 per room for the best double
rm ☕ 85.00/155.00	Full cooked breakfast (whether taken or not) is included in the price of the room
suites 150.00/250.00	Lowest and highest prices for a suite comprising bedroom, bathroom and sitting room

SHORT BREAKS

Many hotels now offer a special rate for a stay of two nights which comprises dinner, room and breakfast usually for a minimum of two people.

SB 105.00/185.00	Prices indicated are lowest and highest per person for two nights.

DEPOSITS – CREDIT CARDS

Some hotels will require a deposit, which confirms the commitment of customer and hotelier alike. Make sure the terms of the agreement are clear.

⬛ ᴁ ⓓ 𝘝𝘐𝘚𝘈	Credit cards accepted by the establishment: Access – American Express – Diners Club – Visa

London

✉ Fulham	Postal address
✆	STD dialling code. Omit 0 when dialling from abroad
BX **A**	Letters giving the location of a place on the town map
⛳₁₈	Golf course and number of holes (handicap usually required; telephone reservation strongly advised)
☀, ≼	Panoramic view, viewpoint
✈	Airport
🚗 ☎ 0345 090700	Motorail connection; further information from telephone number listed
🛈	Tourist Information Centre

Sights – Star rating

★★★	Worth a journey
★★	Worth a detour
★	Interesting

Standard Time

In winter standard time throughout the British Isles is Greenwich Mean Time (G.M.T.). In summer British clocks are advanced by one hour to give British Summer Time (B.S.T.). The actual dates are announced annually but always occur over weekends in March and October.

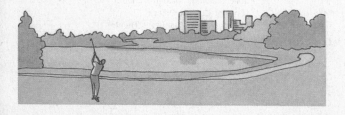

Town plans

@   **Hotels – Restaurants**

Sights

Place of interest and its main entrance
Interesting place of worship

Roads

Motorway
    Interchanges : complete, limited
Dual carriageway with motorway characteristics
Main traffic artery
Primary route
    (network currently being reclassified)
One-way street – Unsuitable for traffic
Pedestrian street
Shopping street – Car park
Gateway – Street passing under arch – Tunnel
Low headroom (16'6" max.) on major through routes
Station and railway
Funicular – Cable-car
Lever bridge – Car ferry

Various signs

Tourist information Centre
Mosque – Synagogue
Communications tower or mast – Ruins
Garden, park, wood – Cemetery
Stadium – Racecourse – Golf course
Golf course (with restrictions for visitors)
View – Panorama
Monument – Fountain – Hospital
Pleasure boat harbour – Lighthouse
Airport – Underground station
Ferry services :
    passengers and cars
Main post office with poste restante, telephone
Public buildings located by letter :
C   County Council Offices
H M T   Town Hall – Museum – Theatre
U   University, College
POL.   Police (in large towns police headquarters)

London

BRENT SOHO   Borough – Area
Borough boundary – Area boundary

Car, tyres

The wearing of seat belts in Great Britain is obligatory for drivers, front seat passengers and rear seat passengers where seat belts are fitted. It is illegal for front seat passengers to carry children on their lap.

CAR MANUFACTURERS AND MICHELIN TYRE SUPPLIERS

A list of the main car manufacturers head offices is contained pages 77 and 78.
In the event of a breakdown the location of your nearest dealer can be obtained by calling the telephone number listed between 9am – 5pm.

ATS Tyre dealers

The address of the nearest ATS tyre dealer can be obtained by contacting the address below between 9am and 5pm.

ATS HOUSE   180-188 Northolt Rd.
Harrow,
Middlesex HA2 OED
(081) 423 2000

MOTORING ORGANISATIONS

The major motoring organisations in Great Britain are the Automobile Association and the Royal Automobile Club. Each provides services in varying degrees for non-resident members of affiliated clubs.

AUTOMOBILE ASSOCIATION
Fanum House
BASINGSTOKE, Hants., RG21 2EA
℘ (0256) 20123

ROYAL AUTOMOBILE CLUB
RAC House, Lansdowne Rd.
CROYDON, Surrey CR9 2JA
℘ (081) 686 2525

Ami lecteur

Cette plaquette « hôtels et restaurants »
réalisée d'après le guide Michelin
« GREAT BRITAIN and IRELAND » 1992
a été conçue spécialement
pour vos voyages à Londres.

Réalisée en toute indépendance,
sa sélection d'hôtels et de restaurants
est le fruit des recherches
de ses inspecteurs,
que complètent
vos précieux courriers et commentaires.

Soucieux d'actualité et de service,
le Guide prépare déjà sa prochaine édition.

Seul le Guide de l'année
mérite ainsi votre confiance.

Pensez à le renouveler...

Pour une visite détaillée de la ville,
utilisez
le guide Vert Michelin « LONDRES ».

Bon séjour
dans la capitale britannique !

Sommaire

Le choix
d'un hôtel, d'un restaurant

Ce guide vous propose une sélection d'hôtels et restaurants
établie à l'usage de l'automobiliste de passage. Les établissements, classés selon leur confort, sont cités par ordre de
préférence dans chaque catégorie.

CATÉGORIES

🏨	Grand luxe et tradition	XXXXX
🏨	Grand confort	XXXX
🏨	Très confortable	XXX
🏨	De bon confort	XX
🏨	Assez confortable	X
🏠	Autre ressource hôtelière conseillée, à prix modérés	
Without rest.	L'hôtel n'a pas de restaurant	
	Le restaurant possède des chambres	with rm

AGRÉMENT ET TRANQUILLITÉ

Certains établissements se distinguent dans le guide par les
symboles rouges indiqués ci-après. Le séjour dans ces hôtels
se révèle particulièrement agréable ou reposant.
Cela peut tenir d'une part au caractère de l'édifice, au décor
original, au site, à l'accueil et aux services qui sont proposés,
d'autre part à la tranquillité des lieux.

🏨 à 🏠	Hôtels agréables
XXXXX à X	Restaurants agréables
« Riverside setting »	Élément particulièrement agréable
🦢	Hôtel très tranquille ou isolé et tranquille
🦢	Hôtel tranquille
≤ London	Vue exceptionnelle
≤	Vue intéressante ou étendue.

L'installation

Les chambres des hôtels que nous recommandons possèdent, en général, des installations sanitaires complètes. Il est toutefois possible que dans les catégories 🏠, 🏠, 🏠 et 🏠, certaines chambres en soient dépourvues.

30 ch	Nombre de chambres
🛗	Ascenseur
▤	Air conditionné
TV	Télévision dans la chambre
⚡	Établissement entièrement ou en partie réservé aux non-fumeurs
☏	Téléphone dans la chambre relié par standard
☎	Téléphone dans la chambre, direct avec l'extérieur
🚶	Chambres accessibles aux handicapés physiques
🏊 🏊	Piscine : de plein air ou couverte
🏋 ⚖s	Salle de remise en forme – Sauna
🌳	Jardin de repos
🎾 🏌9	Tennis à l'hôtel – Golf et nombre de trous
👥 150	Salles de conférences : capacité maximum
🚗	Garage dans l'hôtel (généralement payant)
🅿	Parking réservé à la clientèle
🐕	Accès interdit aux chiens (dans tout ou partie de l'établissement)
Fax	Transmission de documents par télécopie
closed Saturday and August	Fermeture communiquée par le restaurateur
LL35 OSB	Code postal de l'établissement
(Forte)	Chaîne hôtelière (voir liste p. XLII.)

Animaux

L'introduction d'animaux domestiques (chiens, chats...) est interdite en Grande-Bretagne et en Irlande.

La table

LES ÉTOILES

Certains établissements méritent d'être signalés à votre attention pour la qualité de leur cuisine. Nous les distinguons par **les étoiles de bonne table**.

Nous indiquons, pour ces établissements, trois spécialités culinaires qui pourront orienter votre choix.

❀❀❀ | **Une des meilleures tables, vaut le voyage**
Table merveilleuse, grands vins, service impeccable, cadre élégant... Prix en conséquence.

❀❀ | **Table excellente, mérite un détour**
Spécialités et vins de choix... Attendez-vous à une dépense en rapport.

❀ | **Une très bonne table dans sa catégorie**
L'étoile marque une bonne étape sur votre itinéraire.
Mais ne comparez pas l'étoile d'un établissement de luxe à prix élevés avec celle d'une petite maison où à prix raisonnables, on sert également une cuisine de qualité.

LE « M » ROUGE

Tout en appréciant les tables à « étoiles », on peut souhaiter trouver sur sa route un repas plus simple mais toujours de préparation soignée. Certaines maisons nous ont paru répondre à cette préoccupation.

Un « M » rouge les signale à votre attention dans le texte de ce guide.

La vente de boissons alcoolisées

En Grande-Bretagne et en Irlande, la vente de boissons alcoolisées est soumise à des lois pouvant varier d'une région à l'autre.

D'une façon générale, les hôtels, les restaurants et les pubs peuvent demeurer ouverts l'après-midi et servir des boissons alcoolisées dans la mesure où elles accompagnent un repas suffisamment consistant. Les bars ferment après 23 heures. Néanmoins, l'hôtelier a toujours la possibilité de servir, à sa clientèle, des boissons alcoolisées en dehors des heures légales.

Les enfants au-dessous de 14 ans n'ont pas accès aux bars.

Les prix

Les prix que nous indiquons dans ce guide ont été établis en automne 1991. Ils sont susceptibles de modifications, notamment en cas de variations des prix des biens et services.

Entrez à l'hôtel le guide à la main, vous montrerez ainsi qu'il vous conduit là en confiance.

Les prix sont indiqués en livres sterling (1 L = 100 pence). Lorsque les mentions **s., t.**, ou **st.** ne figurent pas, les prix indiqués peuvent être majorés d'un pourcentage pour le service, la T.V.A., ou les deux.

Les hôtels et restaurants figurent en gros caractères lorsque les hôteliers nous ont donné tous leurs prix et se sont engagés, sous leur propre responsabilité, à les appliquer aux touristes de passage porteurs de notre guide.

REPAS

M 13.00/24.00	**Repas à prix fixe** – Déjeuner 13.00, dîner 24.00. Ces prix s'entendent couvert compris
M 15.00/25.00	Voir page 17
s.	Service compris
t.	T.V.A. comprise
st.	Service et T.V.A. compris (prix nets)
🍶 6.00	Prix de la 1/2 bouteille ou carafe de vin ordinaire
M à la carte 20.00/25.00	**Repas à la carte** – Le 1ᵉʳ prix correspond à un repas simple mais soigné, comprenant : petite entrée, plat du jour garni, dessert. Le 2ᵉ prix concerne un repas plus complet, comprenant : hors-d'œuvre, plat principal, fromage ou dessert. Ces prix s'entendent couvert compris
☕ 8.50	Prix du petit déjeuner à l'anglaise, s'il n'est pas compris dans celui de la chambre. Un petit déjeuner continental peut être obtenu à moindre prix

⌂: Dans les établissements de cette catégorie, le dîner est servi à heure fixe exclusivement aux personnes ayant une chambre. Le menu, à prix unique, offre un choix limité de plats. Le déjeuner est rarement proposé. Beaucoup de ces établissements ne sont pas autorisés à vendre des boissons alcoolisées.

CHAMBRES

rm 80.00/150.00	Prix minimum 80.00 d'une chambre pour une personne et prix maximum 150.00 de la plus belle chambre occupée par deux personnes
rm ☕ 85.00/155.00	Le prix du petit déjeuner à l'anglaise est inclus dans le prix de la chambre, même s'il n'est pas consommé
suites 150.00/250.00	Prix minimum et maximum d'un appartement comprenant chambre, salle de bains et salon

« SHORT BREAKS »

| SB 105.00/ 185.00 | Prix minimum et maximum par personne pour un séjour de deux nuits en conditions avantageuses ou « Short Break ». Ce forfait comprend la chambre, le dîner et le petit déjeuner, en général pour un minimum de deux personnes. |

LES ARRHES – CARTES DE CRÉDIT

Certains hôteliers demandent le versement d'arrhes. Il s'agit d'un dépôt-garantie qui engage l'hôtelier comme le client. Bien faire préciser les dispositions de cette garantie.

| ⑤ AE ⑩ VISA | Cartes de crédit acceptées par l'établissement : Access (Eurocard) – American Express – Diners Club – Visa |

Londres

✉ Fulham	Bureau de poste desservant la localité
✆	Indicatif téléphonique interurbain (de l'étranger, ne pas composer le 0)
BX **A**	Lettres repérant un emplacement sur le plan
⛳₁₈	Golf et nombre de trous (Handicap généralement demandé, réservation par téléphone vivement recommandée)
☀, ←	Panorama, point de vue
✈	Aéroport
🚗 ✆ 0345 090700	Localité desservie par train-auto. Renseignements au numéro de téléphone indiqué
🛈	Information touristique

Les curiosités

★★★	Vaut le voyage
★★	Mérite un détour
★	Intéressant

Heure légale

Les visiteurs devront tenir compte de l'heure officielle en Grande Bretagne : une heure de retard sur l'heure française.

Les plans

@   **Hôtels – Restaurants**

Curiosités

Bâtiment intéressant et entrée principale
Édifice religieux intéressant

Voirie

M 1   Autoroute
     échangeurs : complet, partiel
Route à chaussées séparées de type autoroutier
Grand axe de circulation
A 2   Itinéraire principal (Primary route)
     réseau en cours de révision
Sens unique – Rue impraticable
Rue piétonne
Piccadilly P   Rue commerçante – Parc de stationnement
Porte – Passage sous voûte – Tunnel
15'5   Passage bas (inférieur à 16'6") sur les grandes voies de circulation
Gare et voie ferrée
Funiculaire – Téléphérique, télécabine
B   Pont mobile – Bac pour autos

Signes divers

Information touristique
Mosquée – Synagogue
Tour ou pylône de télécommunication – Ruines
Jardin, parc, bois – Cimetière
Stade – Hippodrome – Golf
Golf (réservé)
Vue – Panorama
Monument – Fontaine – Hôpital
Port de plaisance – Phare
Aéroport – Station de métro
Transport par bateau :
     passagers et voitures
Bureau principal de poste restante, téléphone
Bâtiment public repéré par une lettre :
C   Bureau de l'Administration du Comté
H M T   Hôtel de ville – Musée – Théâtre
U   Université, grande école
POL   Police (commissariat central)

Londres

BRENT SOHO   Nom d'arrondissement (borough) – de quartier (area)
Limite de « borough » – d'« area »

La voiture, les pneus

En Grande-Bretagne, le port de la ceinture de sécurité est obligatoire pour le conducteur et le passager avant ainsi qu'à l'arrière, si le véhicule en est équipé. La loi interdit au passager avant de prendre un enfant sur ses genoux.

MARQUES AUTOMOBILES
FOURNISSEURS DE PNEUS MICHELIN

Une liste des principales marques automobiles figure pages 77 et 78.
En cas de panne, l'adresse du plus proche agent de la marque vous sera communiquée en appelant le numéro de téléphone indiqué, entre 9 h et 17 h.

ATS Spécialistes du pneu

Des renseignements sur le plus proche point de vente de pneus ATS pourront être obtenus en s'informant entre 9 h et 17 h à l'adresse indiquée ci-dessous.

ATS HOUSE	180-188 Northolt Rd.
	Harrow,
	Middlesex HA2 OED
	(081) 423 2000

Dans nos agences, nous nous faisons un plaisir de donner à nos clients tous conseils pour la meilleure utilisation de leurs pneus.

AUTOMOBILE CLUBS

Les principales organisations de secours automobile dans le pays sont l'Automobile Association et le Royal Automobile Club, toutes deux offrant certains de leurs services aux membres de clubs affiliés.

AUTOMOBILE ASSOCIATION	ROYAL AUTOMOBILE CLUB
Fanum House	RAC House, Lansdowne Rd,
BASINGSTOKE, Hants., RG21 2EA	CROYDON, Surrey CR9 2JA
☎ (0256) 20123	☎ (081) 686 2525

Amico Lettore

Questa pubblicazione alberghi e ristoranti
ricavata dalla guida Michelin
« GREAT BRITAIN and IRELAND » 1992,
è stata realizzata appositamente
per i vostri viaggi a Londra.

La sua selezione di alberghi
e ristoranti, realizzata in assoluta
indipendenza, è il risultato
delle indagini dei suoi ispettori,
che completano
le vostre preziose informazioni
e giudizi.

Desiderosa di mantenersi sempre
aggiornata per fornire un buon
servizio, la Guida sta già
preparando la sua prossima edizione.

Soltanto la Guida dell'anno
merita perciò la vostra fiducia.
Pensate a rinnovarla...

Per una visita turistica della città utilizzate
la guida verde Michelin « LONDON »,
disponibile in inglese ed in francese.

Buon soggiorno nella capitale britannica !

Sommario

La scelta
di un albergo, di un ristorante

Questa guida Vi propone una selezione di alberghi e ristoranti stabilita ad uso dell'automobilista di passaggio. Gli esercizi, classificati in base al confort che offrono, vengono citati in ordine di preferenza per ogni categoria.

CATEGORIE

🏨🏨🏨	Gran lusso e tradizione	XXXXX
🏨🏨🏨	Gran confort	XXXX
🏨🏨	Molto confortevole	XXX
🏨🏨	Di buon confort	XX
🏨	Abbastanza confortevole	X
🏠	Altra risorsa, consigliata per prezzi contenuti	
without rest.	L'albergo non ha ristorante	
	Il ristorante dispone di camere	with rm

AMENITÀ E TRANQUILLITÀ

Alcuni esercizi sono evidenziati nella guida dai simboli rossi indicati qui di seguito. Il soggiorno in questi alberghi dovrebbe rivelarsi particolarmente ameno o riposante.
Ciò può dipendere sia dalle caratteristiche dell'edifico, dalle decorazioni non comuni, dalla sua posizione e dal servizio offerto, sia dalla tranquillità dei luoghi.

🏨🏨🏨 a 🏠	Alberghi ameni
XXXXX a X	Ristoranti ameni
« Riverside setting »	Un particolare piacevole
🐾	Albergo molto tranquillo o isolato e tranquillo
🐾	Albergo tranquillo
≤ London	Vista eccezionale
≤	Vista interessante o estesa

Installazioni

Le camere degli alberghi che raccomandiamo possiedono, generalmente, delle installazioni sanitarie complete. È possibile tuttavia che nelle categorie 🏠, 🏠, ☆ e ⌂ alcune camere ne siano sprovviste.

30 rm	Numero di camere
🛗	Ascensore
▤	Aria condizionata
TV	Televisione in camera
⚞	Esercizio riservato completamente o in parte ai non fumatori
☏	Telefono in camera collegato con il centralino
☎	Telefono in camera comunicante direttamente con l'esterno
🦽	Camere di agevole accesso per i minorati fisici
⤢ ▨	Piscina : all'aperto, coperta
🏋 ⛲	Palestra – Sauna
🌳	Giardino da riposo
✗ ⛳	Tennis appartenente all'albergo – Golf e numero di buche
🏛 150	Sale per conferenze : capienza massima
🚗	Garage nell'albergo (generalmente a pagamento)
℗	Parcheggio riservato alla clientela
⛝	Accesso vietato ai cani (in tutto o in parte dell'esercizio)
Fax	Trasmissione telefonica di documenti
closed Saturday and August	Periodo di chiusura, comunicato dall'albergatore
LL35 OSB	Codice postale dell' esercizio
(Forte)	Catena alberghiera (Vedere la lista p. XLII.)

Animali

L'introduzione di animali domestici (cani, gatti...), in Gran Bretagna e in Irlanda, è vietata.

La tavola

LE STELLE

Alcuni esercizi meritano di essere segnalati alla Vostra attenzione per la qualità tutta particolare della loro cucina. Noi li evidenziamo con le « **stelle di ottima tavola** ». Per questi ristoranti indichiamo tre specialità culinarie e alcuni vini locali che potranno aiutarVi nella scelta.

❀❀❀ | **Una delle migliori tavole, vale il viaggio**
Tavola meravigliosa, grandi vini, servizio impeccabile, ambientazione accurata... Prezzi conformi.

❀❀ | **Tavola eccellente, merita una deviazione**
Specialità e vini scelti... AspettateVi una spesa in proporzione.

❀ | **Un'ottima tavola nella sua categoria**
La stella indica una tappa gastronomica sul Vostro itinerario. Non mettete però a confronto la stella di un esercizio di lusso, dai prezzi elevati, con quella di un piccolo esercizio dove, a prezzi ragionevoli, viene offerta una cucina di qualità.

LA « M » ROSSA

Pur apprezzando le tavole a « stella », si desidera alle volte consumare un pasto più semplice ma sempre accuratamente preparato.
Alcuni esercizi ci son parsi rispondenti a tale esigenza e sono contraddistinti nella guida da una « M » in rosso.

La vendita di bevande alcoliche

In Gran Bretagna e Irlanda la vendita di bevande alcoliche è soggetta a leggi che possono variare da una regione all'altra. In generale gli alberghi, i ristoranti e i pubs possono restare aperti il pomeriggio e servire bevande alcoliche nella misura in cui queste accompagnano un pasto abbastanza consistente. I bars chiudono dopo le ore 23.00.
L'albergatore ha tuttavia la possibilità di servire alla clientela bevande alcoliche anche oltre le ore legali.
Ai ragazzi inferiori ai 14 anni è vietato l'accesso ai bar.

I prezzi

I prezzi che indichiamo in questa guida sono stati stabiliti nel l'autunno 1991. Potranno pertanto subire delle variazioni in relazione ai cambiamenti dei prezzi di beni e servizi.

Entrate nell'albergo o nel ristorante con la guida alla mano, dimostrando in tal modo la fiducia in chi vi ha indirizzato.

Gli alberghi e i ristoranti vengono menzionati in carattere grassetto quando gli albergatori ci hanno comunicato tutti i loro prezzi e si sono impegnati, sotto la propria responsabilità, ad applicarli ai turisti di passaggio, in possesso della nostra guida.

I prezzi sono indicati in lire sterline (1 £ = 100 pence).

Quando non figurano le lettere **s.**, **t.**, o **st.** i prezzi indicati possono essere maggiorati per il servizio o per l'I.V.A. o per entrambi.

PASTI

M 13.00/24.00	**Prezzo fisso** – Pranzo 13.00, cena 24.00. Questi prezzi comprendono il coperto
M 15.00/25.00	Vedere p. 27
s.	Servizio compreso
t.	I.V.A. compresa
st.	Servizio ed I.V.A. compresi (prezzi netti)
⚱ 6.00	Prezzo della mezza bottiglia o di una caraffa di vino
M a la carte 20.00/25.00	**Alla carta** – Il 1° prezzo corrisponde ad un pasto semplice comprendente : primo piatto, piatto del giorno con contorno, dessert. Il 2° prezzo corrisponde ad un pasto più completo comprendente : antipasto, piatto principale, formaggio e dessert Questi prezzi comprendono il coperto
� 8.50	Prezzo della prima colazione inglese se non è compreso nel prezzo della camera. Una prima colazione continentale può essere ottenuta a minor prezzo

⌂ : Negli alberghi di questa categoria, la cena viene servita, ad un'ora stabilita, esclusivamente a chi vi alloggia. Il menu, a prezzo fisso, offre una scelta limitata di piatti. Raramente viene servito anche il pranzo. Molti di questi esercizi non hanno l'autorizzazione a vendere alcolici.

CAMERE

rm 80.00/ 150.00	Prezzo minimo 80.00 per una camera singola e prezzo massimo 150.00 per la camera più bella per due persone
rm ⊏⊐ 85.00/155.00	Il prezzo della prima colazione inglese è compreso nel prezzo della camera anche se non viene consumata
suites 150.00/250.00	Prezzo minimo e massimo per un appartamento comprendente camera, bagno e salone

SB 105.00/ | Prezzo minimo e massimo per persona per un
185.00 | soggiorno di due notti a condizioni vantaggiose o « Short Break ». Questo forfait comprende la camera, la cena e la colazione del mattino generalmente per un minimo di due persone.

LA CAPARRA - CARTE DI CREDITO

Alcuni albergatori chiedono il versamento di una caparra. Si tratta di un deposito-garanzia che impegna tanto l'albergatore che il cliente. Vi raccomandiamo di farVi precisare le norme riguardanti la reciproca garanzia di tale caparra.

🔲 🄰🄴 🄾 *VISA* | Carte di credito accettate dall'esercizio
Access (Eurocard) – American Express – Diners Club – Visa

Londra

✉ Fulham	Sede dell'ufficio postale
✆	Prefisso telefonico interurbano. Dall'estero non formare lo 0
BX **A**	Lettere indicanti l'ubicazione sulla pianta
⛳18	Golf e numero di buche (handicap generalmente richiesto, prenotazione telefonica vivamente consigliata)
❀ ≼	Panorama, punto di vista
✈	Aeroporto
🚗 ✆ 0345 090700	Località con servizio auto su treno. Informarsi al numero di telefono indicato
🅸	Ufficio informazioni turistiche

Le curiosità

★★★	Vale il viaggio
★★	Merita una deviazione
★	Interessante

Ora legale

I visitatori dovranno tenere in considerazione l'ora ufficiale in Gran Bretagna : un'ora di ritardo sull'ora italiana.

Le piante

@   **Alberghi – Ristoranti**

Curiosità

Edificio interessante ed entrata principale
Costruzione religiosa interessante

Viabilità

Autostrada
    svincoli : completo, parziale,
Strada a carreggiate separate di tipo autostradale
Asse principale di circolazione
Itinerario principale
(« Primary route », rete stradale in corso di revisione)
Senso unico – Via impraticabile
Via pedonale
Piccadilly   Via commerciale – Parcheggio
Porta – Sottopassaggio – Galleria
Sottopassaggio (altezza inferiore a 16'6") sulle grandi
vie di circolazione
Stazione e ferrovia
Funicolare – Funivia, Cabinovia
Ponte mobile – Battello per auto

Simboli vari

Ufficio informazioni turistiche
Moschea – Sinagoga
Torre o pilone per telecomunicazione – Ruderi
Giardino, parco, bosco – Cimitero
Stadio – Ippodromo – Golf
Golf riservato
Vista – Panorama
Monumento – Fontana – Ospedale
Porto per imbarcazioni da diporto – Faro
Aeroporto – Stazione della Metropolitana
Trasporto con traghetto :
    passeggeri ed autovetture
Ufficio centrale di fermo posta, telefono
Edificio pubblico indicato con lettera :
C   Sede dell'Amministrazione di Contea
H M T   Municipio – Museo – Teatro
U   Università, grande scuola
POL   Polizia (Questura, nelle grandi città)

Londra

BRENT SOHO   Nome del distretto amministrativo (borough) –
del quartiere (area)
Limite del « borough » – di « area »

L'automobile, I pneumatici

In Gran Bretagna, l'uso delle cinture di sicurezza è obbligatorio per il conducente e il passeggero del sedile anteriore, nonchè per i sedili posteriori, se ne sono equipaggiati. La legge non consente al passeggero d'avanti di tenere un bambino sulle ginocchia.

MARCHE AUTOMOBILISTICHE, RIVENDITORI DI PNEUMATICI MICHELIN

L'elenco delle principali case automobilistiche si trova alle pagine 77 e 78.
In caso di necessità l'indirizzo della più vicina officina autorizzata vi sarà comunicato chiamando, dalle 9 alle 17, il numero telefonico indicato.

ATS Specialista in pneumatici

Potrete avere delle informazioni sul più vicino punto vendita di pneumatici ATS, rivolgendovi, tra le 9 e le 17, all'indirizzo indicato qui di seguito :

ATS HOUSE   180-188 Northolt Rd.
                Harrow,
                Middlesex HA2 OED
                (081) 423 2000

Le nostre Succursali sono in grado di dare ai nostri clienti tutti i consigli relativi alla migliore utilizzazione dei pneumatici.

AUTOMOBILE CLUBS

Le principali organizzazioni di soccorso automobilistico sono l'Automobile Association ed il Royal Automobile Club : entrambe offrono alcuni loro servizi ai membri dei club affiliati.

AUTOMOBILE ASSOCIATION   ROYAL AUTOMOBILE CLUB
Fanum House   RAC House, Lansdowne Rd,
BASINGSTOKE, Hants., RG21 2EA   CROYDON, Surrey CR9 2JA
☏ (0256) 20123   ☏ (081) 686 2525

Lieber Leser

*Speziell für Ihren London-Besuch
ist dieser Auszug
aus dem Michelin-Führer
« Great Britain and Ireland »
1992 gedacht.*

*Er bringt eine
in voller Unabhängigkeit getroffene,
bewußt begrenzte Auswahl
an Hotels und Restaurants.
Sie basiert auf den regelmäßigen
Überprüfungen durch unsere Inspektoren,
komplettiert durch die zahlreichen
Zuschriften und Erfahrungsberichte
unserer Leser.*

*Wir sind stets um die Aktualität
unserer Informationen bemüht
und bereiten schon jetzt
den Führer des nächsten Jahres vor.
Nur die neueste Ausgabe
ist wirklich zuverlässig –
denken Sie bitte daran,
wenn der nächste
Rote Michelin-Führer erscheint.*

*Eine detaillierte Stadtbeschreibung
finden Sie im
Grünen Michelin-Reiseführer « London »
(in englischer und französischer Ausgabe).*

*Wir wünschen Ihnen
einen angenehmen Aufenthalt
in der Hauptstadt von Großbritannien.*

Inhaltsverzeichnis

Wahl
eines Hotels, eines Restaurants

Die Auswahl der in diesem Führer aufgeführten Hotels und Restaurants ist für Durchreisende gedacht. In jeder Kategorie drückt die Reihenfolge der Betriebe (sie sind nach ihrem Komfort klassifiziert) eine weitere Rangordnung aus.

KATEGORIEN

🏨	Großer Luxus und Tradition	XXXXX
🏨	Großer Komfort	XXXX
🏨	Sehr komfortabel	XXX
🏨	Mit gutem Komfort	XX
🏨	Mit ausreichendem Komfort	X
⚇	Preiswerte, empfehlenswerte Gasthäuser und Pensionen	

without rest. Hotel ohne Restaurant

Restaurant vermietet auch Zimmer   with rm

ANNEHMLICHKEITEN

Manche Häuser sind im Führer durch rote Symbole gekennzeichnet (s. unten). Der Aufenthalt in diesen Hotels ist wegen der schönen, ruhigen Lage, der nicht alltäglichen Einrichtung und Atmosphäre und dem gebotenen Service besonders angenehm und erholsam.

🏨 bis ⚇	Angenehme Hotels
XXXXX bis X	Angenehme Restaurants
« Riverside setting »	Besondere Annehmlichkeit
🐾	Sehr ruhiges, oder abgelegenes und ruhiges Hotel
🐾	Ruhiges Hotel
≼ London	Reizvolle Aussicht
≼	Interessante oder weite Sicht

Einrichtung

Die meisten der empfohlenen Hotels verfügen über Zimmer, die alle oder doch zum größten Teil mit einer Naßzelle ausgestattet sind. In den Häusern der Kategorien 🏨, 🏠, 🕭 und ↑ kann diese jedoch in einigen Zimmern fehlen.

30 rm	Anzahl der Zimmer
|$|	Fahrstuhl
▤	Klimaanlage
TV	Fernsehen im Zimmer
⊱✕	Hotel ganz oder teilweise reserviert für Nichtraucher
☏	Zimmertelefon mit Außenverbindung über Telefonzentrale
☎	Zimmertelefon mit direkter Außenverbindung
⅋	Für Körperbehinderte leicht zugängliche Zimmer
⌇ ⊠	Freibad, Hallenbad
⌧ ⇶	Fitneßcenter – Sauna
⪥	Liegewiese, Garten
✕ ⎋₉	Hoteleigener Tennisplatz – Golfplatz und Lochzahl
⚒ 150	Konferenzräume : Höchstkapazität
⇔	Hotelgarage (wird gewöhnlich berechnet)
℗	Parkplatz reserviert für Gäste
✕	Hunde sind unerwünscht (im ganzen Haus bzw. in den Zimmern oder im Restaurant)
Fax	Telefonische Dokumentenübermittlung
closed Saturday and August	Schließungszeit, vom Hotelier mitgeteilt
LL35 OSB	Angabe des Postbezirks (hinter der Hoteladresse)
(Forte)	Hotelkette (Liste Seite XLII.)

Tiere

Das Mitführen von Haustieren (Hunde, Katzen u. dgl.) bei der Einreise in Großbritannien und Irland ist untersagt.

Küche

DIE STERNE

Einige Häuser verdienen wegen ihrer überdurchschnittlich guten Küche Ihre besondere Beachtung. Auf diese Häuser weisen die Sterne hin.

Bei den mit « **Stern** » ausgezeichneten Betrieben nennen wir drei kulinarische Spezialitäten, die Sie probieren sollten.

❀❀❀ | **Eine der besten Küchen : eine Reise wert**
Ein denkwürdiges Essen, edle Weine, tadelloser Service, gepflegte Atmosphäre ... entsprechende Preise.

❀❀ | **Eine hervorragende Küche : verdient einen Umweg**
Ausgesuchte Menus und Weine ... angemessene Preise.

❀ | **Eine sehr gute Küche : verdient Ihre besondere Beachtung**
Der Stern bedeutet eine angenehme Unterbrechung Ihrer Reise. Vergleichen Sie aber bitte nicht den Stern eines sehr teuren Luxusrestaurants mit dem Stern eines kleineren oder mittleren Hauses, wo man Ihnen zu einem annehmbaren Preis eine ebenfalls vorzügliche Mahlzeit reicht.

DAS ROTE « M »

Wir glauben, daß Sie neben den Häusen mit « Stern » auch solche Adressen interessieren werden, die einfache, aber sorgfältig zubereitete Mahlzeiten anbieten.

Auf solche Häuser weisen wir im Text durch das rote « M » hin.

Ausschank alkoholischer Getränke

In Großbritannien und Irland unterliegt der Ausschank alkoholischer Getränke gesetzlichen Bestimmungen, die in den einzelnen Gegenden verschieden sind.

Generell können Hotels, Restaurants und Pubs nachmittags geöffnet sein und alkoholische Getränke ausschenken, wenn diese zu einer entsprechend gehaltvollen Mahlzeit genossen werden. Die Bars schließen nach 23 Uhr.

Hotelgästen können alkoholische Getränke jedoch auch außerhalb der Ausschankzeiten serviert werden.

Kindern unter 14 Jahren ist der Zutritt zu den Bars untersagt.

Preise

Die in diesem Führer genannten Preise wurden uns im Herbst 1991 angegeben. Sie können sich mit den Preisen von Waren und Dienstleistungen ändern.
Halten Sie beim Betreten des Hotels den Führer in der Hand. Sie zeigen damit, daß Sie aufgrund dieser Empfehlung gekommen sind.
Die Preise sind in Pfund Sterling angegeben (1 £ = 100 pence). Wenn die Buchstaben **s.**, **t.**, oder **st.** nicht hinter den angegebenen Preisen aufgeführt sind, können sich diese um den Zuschlag für Bedienung und/oder MWSt erhöhen.
Die Namen der Hotels und Restaurants, die ihre Preise genannt haben, sind fett gedruckt. Gleichzeitig haben sich diese Häuser verpflichtet, die von den Hoteliers selbst angegebenen Preise den Benutzern des Michelin-Führers zu berechnen.

MAHLZEITEN

M 13.00/24.00	**Feste Menupreise** – Mittagessen 13.00, Abendessen 24.00 (inkl. Couvert)
M 15.00/25.00	Siehe Seite 37
s.	Bedienung inkl.
t.	MWSt inkl.
st.	Bedienung und MWSt inkl.
♨ 6.00	Preis für 1/2 Flasche oder eine Karaffe Tafelwein
M a la carte 20.00/25.00	**Mahlzeiten « à la carte »** – Der erste Preis entspricht einer einfachen aber sorgfältig zubereiteten Mahlzeit, bestehend aus kleiner Vorspeise, Tagesgericht mit Beilage und Nachtisch. Der zweite Preis entspricht einer reichlicheren Mahlzeit mit Vorspeise, Hauptgericht, Käse oder Nachtisch (inkl. Couvert)
⌑ 8.50	Preis des englischen Frühstücks, wenn dieser nicht im Übernachtungspreis enthalten ist. Einfaches, billigeres Frühstück (Continental breakfast) erhältlich

⌂ : In dieser Hotelkategorie wird ein Abendessen normalerweise nur zu bestimmten Zeiten für Hotelgäste angeboten. Es besteht aus einem Menu mit begrenzter Auswahl zu festgesetztem Preis. Mittagessen wird selten angeboten. Viele dieser Hotels sind nicht berechtigt, alkoholische Getränke auszuschenken.

ZIMMER

rm 80.00/ 150.00	Mindestpreis 80.00 für ein Einzelzimmer und Höchstpreis 150.00 für das schönste Doppelzimmer
rm ⌑ 85.00/155.00	Übernachtung mit englischem Frühstück, selbst wenn dieses nicht eingenommen wird
suites 150.00/250.00	Mindest- und Höchstpreis für ein Appartement bestehend aus Wohnzimmer, Schlafzimmer und Bad

SB 105.00/
185.00 | Mindest- und Höchstpreis pro Person bei einem Aufenthalt von 2 Nächten (« Short Break »). Diese Pauschalpreise (für mindestens 2 Personen) umfassen Zimmer, Abendessen und Frühstück.

ANZAHLUNG – KREDITKARTEN

Einige Hoteliers verlangen eine Anzahlung. Diese ist als Garantie sowohl für den Hotelier als auch für den Gast anzusehen.

⬛ AE ① VISA | Vom Haus akzeptierte Kreditkarten :
Access (Eurocard) – American Express – Diners Club – Visa (Carte Bleue)

London

✉ Fulham | Zuständiges Postamt
✆ | Vorwahlnummer (bei Gesprächen vom Ausland aus wird die erste Null weggelassen)
BX **A** | Markierung auf dem Stadtplan
⏸18 | Öffentlicher Golfplatz und Lochzahl (Handicap erforderlich, telefonische Reservierung empfehlenswert)
☀, ≤ | Rundblick, Aussichtspunkt
✈ | Flughafen
🚗 ✆ 0345 090700 | Ladestelle für Autoreisezüge – Nähere Auskünfte unter der angegebenen Telefonnummer
🛈 | Informationsstelle

Sehenswürdigkeiten

★★★ | Eine Reise wert
★★ | Verdient einen Umweg
★ | Sehenswert

Uhrzeit

In Großbritannien ist eine Zeitverschiebung zu beachten und die Uhr gegenüber der deutschen Zeit um 1 Stunde zurückzustellen.

Stadtpläne

@	**Hotels – Restaurants**

Sehenswürdigkeiten

Sehenswertes Gebäude mit Haupteingang
Sehenswerter Sakralbau

Straßen

M 1	Autobahn
4 4	Anschlußstellen : Autobahneinfahrt und/oder-ausfahrt, Schnellstraße mit getrennten Fahrbahnen
	Hauptverkehrsstraße
A 2	Fernverkehrsstraße (Primary route) Netz wird z.z. neu eingestuft
◄ ≍≍≍≍≍	Einbahnstraße – nicht befahrbare Straße
	Fußgängerzone
Piccadilly P	Einkaufsstraße – Parkplatz
╬ ╪╞ ╪╞	Tor – Passage – Tunnel
15.9	Unterführung (Höhe angegeben bis 16'6") auf Hauptverkehrsstraßen
▬ 🚆	Bahnhof und Bahnlinie
o+++++o o-●-●-o	Standseilbahn – Seilschwebebahn
△ B	Bewegliche Brücke – Autofähre

Sonstige Zeichen

🛈	Informationsstelle
☪ ✡	Moschee – Synagoge
📡 ⁂	Funk-, Fernsehturm – Ruine
🗺 ⁑⁑	Garten, Park, Wäldchen – Friedhof
◯ 🏇 ⓕ	Stadion – Pferderennbahn – Golfplatz
⚑	Golfplatz (Zutritt bedingt erlaubt)
◄ᶘ ⛛ᶘ	Aussicht – Rundblick
■ ◉ ✚	Denkmal – Brunnen – Krankenhaus
⚓ ⚑	Jachthafen – Leuchtturm
✈ ⊖ ●	Flughafen – U-Bahnstation
🚢	Schiffsverbindungen : Autofähre
✉	Hauptpostamt (postlagernde Sendungen), Telefon
⌂	Öffentliches Gebäude, durch einen Buchstaben gekennzeichnet :
C	Sitz der Grafschaftsverwaltung
H M T	Rathaus – Museum – Theater
U	Universität, Hochschule
POL	Polizei (in größeren Städten Polizeipräsidium)

London

BRENT SOHO	Name des Verwaltungsbezirks (borough) – des Stadtteils (area)
	Grenze des « borough » – des « area »

Das Auto, die Reifen

In Großbritannien herrscht Anschnallpflicht für Fahrer, Beifahrer und auf dem Rücksitz, wenn Gurte vorhanden sind. Es ist verboten, Kinder auf den Vordersitzen auf dem Schoß zu befördern.

AUTOMOBILFIRMEN
LIEFERANTEN VON MICHELIN-REIFEN

Eine Liste der wichtigsten Automobilhersteller finden Sie auf den Seiten 77 und 78.
Im Pannenfall erfahren Sie zwischen 9⁰⁰ und 17⁰⁰ die Adresse der nächstgelegenen Vertrags werkstatt, wenn Sie die angegebene Rufnummer wählen.

ATS Reifenhändler

Die Anschrift der nächstgelegenen ATS-Verkaufsstelle erhalten Sie auf Anfrage (9-17 Uhr) bei

ATS HOUSE   180-188 Northolt Rd.
                 Harrow,
                 Middlesex HA2 OED
                 (081) 423 2000

AUTOMOBILCLUBS

Die wichtigsten Automobilclubs des Landes sind die Automobile Association und der Royal Automobile Club, die den Mitgliedern der der FIA angeschlossenen Automobilclubs Pannenhilfe leisten und einige ihrer Dienstleistungen anbieten.

AUTOMOBILE ASSOCIATION   ROYAL AUTOMOBILE CLUB
Fanum House   RAC House, Lansdowne Rd
BASINGSTOKE, Hants., RG21 2EA   CROYDON, Surrey CR9 2JA
☏ (0256) 20123   ☏ (081) 686 2525

Major hotel groups
Abbreviations used in the Guide and central reservation telephone numbe

Principales chaînes hôtelières
Abréviations utilisées dans nos textes et centraux téléphonique
de réservation

Principali catene alberghiere
Abbreviazoni utilizzate nei nostri testi e centrali telefoniche
di prenotazione

Die wichtigsten Hotelketten
Im Führer benutzte Abkürzungen der Hotelketten und ihre
Zentrale für telefonische Reservierung

BEST WESTERN HOTELS	BEST WESTERN	081 (London) 541 00: 041 (Glasgow) 204 17: 061 (Manchester) 834 54
CHEF & BREWER HOTELS	CHEF & BREWER	
(No central reservations – Contact Hotels direct)		
COPTHORNE	COPTHORNE	0800 414741 (Toll Fre
DE VERE HOTELS PLC	DE VERE	0925 (Warrington) 650:
EDWARDIAN HOTELS	EDWARDIAN	081 (London) 564 88:
FORTE HOTELS	FORTE	(0345) 500400
HILTON HOTELS	HILTON	071 (London) 734 6000
HOLIDAY INN WORLDWIDE	HOLIDAY INN	071 (London) 722 7755
INTERCONTINENTAL HOTELS LTD	INTER-CON	081 (London) 847 2277 calls from outside Lond 0345 581444
JARVIS	JARVIS	(0345) 581811
LANSBURY HOTELS	LANSBURY	0582 (Luton) 400158
MOUNT CHARLOTTE THISTLE HOTELS	MT. CHARLOTTE THISTLE	071 (London) 937 80: 0532 (Leeds) 444866
NOVOTEL	NOVOTEL	071 (London) 724 10:
QUEENS MOAT HOUSES PLC	Q.M.H.	0800 289330 (Toll Free) 0708 (Romford) 7666
RAMADA INTERNATIONAL	RAMADA	0800 181737 (Toll Free) 071 (London) 235 52:
RANK HOTELS	RANK	081 (London) 569 7120 /7211
RESORT HOTELS PLC	RESORT	(0345) 313213
SHERATON HOTELS	SHERATON	071 (London) 7310315
STAKIS HOTELS	STAKIS	0800 262626 (Toll Fre
SWALLOW HOTELS LTD	SWALLOW	091 (Tyneside) 529 46
TOBY HOTELS	TOBY	
(No central reservations – Contact Hotels direct)		

London

ONDON (Greater) Michelin Map **404** folds 42 to 44 – London G. – pop. 7 566 620 – ◑ 071 or
081 : see heading of each area.

✈ Heathrow, ✆ (081) 759 4321, Telex 934892, p. 8 AX – **Terminal :** Airbus (A1) from Victoria,
bus (A2) from Paddington – Underground (Piccadilly line) frequent service daily.

✈ Gatwick, ✆ 0293 (Crawley) 28822 and ✆ 081 (London) 668 4211, Telex 877725, p. 9 : by
₹3 EZ and M 23 – **Terminal :** Coach service from Victoria Coach Station (Flightline 777 hourly
vice) – Railink (Gatwick Express) from Victoria (24 h service).

✈ London City Airport ✆ (071) 589 5599, Telex 264731, p. 7 HV.

✈ Stansted at Bishop's Stortford, ✆ 0279 (Bishop's Stortford) 680800, Telex 818708, NE :
m. p. 7 : by M 11 JT and A 120.

itish Airways, Victoria Air Terminal : 115 Buckingham Palace Rd, SW1, ✆ (071) 834 9411,
32 BX.

🚆 Euston and Paddington ✆ 0345 090700.

National Tourist Information Centre, Victoria Station Forecourt, SW1, ✆ (071) 730 3488.
tish Travel Centre, 12 Regent St., Piccadilly Circus, SW1 ✆ (071) 730 3400.
ndon Tourist Board and Convention Bureau Telephone Information Services ✆ (071) 730 3488.

OME PRACTICAL ADVICE

Parking in central London, although available, is difficult to find and expensive. Public
Transport - bus or Underground - is much more practical. Full details of these services can
be obtained from London Transport Travel Enquiries, 55 Broadway, SW1, ✆ (071) 222 1234.
In most instances **taxi-cabs,** when showing the illuminated « For Hire » sign, will pick up
passengers in the streets on demand. Alternatively they may be called by telephone. Consult
your Hotel Porter.

Theatre bookings and car hire : Your hotel can help you, either directly, or by giving
agency addresses.

UELQUES RENSEIGNEMENTS PRATIQUES

Le stationnement dans le centre de Londres, bien que possible, est difficile et onéreux.
Ainsi les transports en commun, bus ou métro, sont-ils beaucoup plus pratiques. Pour plus
amples renseignements s'adresser au London Transport Travel Enquiries, 55 Broadway,
SW1, ✆ (071) 222 1234.

Dans la plupart des cas, on peut héler les **taxis** munis du voyant lumineux « For Hire » mais il
est possible de les appeler par téléphone. Se renseigner auprès des hôtels.

Places de théâtres et locations de voitures : votre hôtel peut vous venir en aide, soit
directement, soit en vous indiquant l'adresse d'une agence.

UALCHE CONSIGLIO PRATICO

Parcheggiare nel centro di Londra è possibile, ma difficile e costoso. Perciò trasporti
pubblici, autobus o metropolitana, sono assai più pratici. Per maggiori chiarimenti rivolgersi
al London Transport Travel Enquiries, 55 Broadway, SW1, ✆ (071) 222 1234.

Generalmente è possibile fermare a voce un **taxi** che abbia l'indicazione « For Hire », ma si
può anche chiamarlo per telefono. Informarsi all'albergo.

Prenotazioni per teatro e noleggio vetture : il vostro hotel può provvedere sia direttamente,
sia indicandovi l'indirizzo di un' agenzia.

UTZLICHE HINWEISE FÜR DEN AUFENTHALT

Das **Parken** in der Londoner Innenstadt ist zwar möglich, aber teuer, und man findet schwer
einen freien Platz. Die öffentlichen Verkehrsmittel wie Untergrundbahn und Autobus sind
daher vorzuziehen. Nähere Auskünfte erteilt das Londoner Transport Travel Enquiries, 55
Broadway, SW1, ✆ (071) 222 1234.

Taxis mit der Leuchtschrift „For-Hire" können durch Herbeiwinken angehalten werden und
nehmen Fahrgäste auf; sonst bestellt man sie telefonisch. Auskünfte gibt Ihr Hotel.

Sie können die **Reservierung von Theaterplätzen** und das **Mieten eines Leihwagens**
entweder direkt von Ihrem Hotel vornehmen lassen oder sich die Adressen der Agenturen
und Autoverleihe geben lassen.

Sights
Curiosités – Le curiosità
Sehenswürdigkeiten

HISTORIC BUILDINGS AND MONUMENTS

Palace of Westminster★★★ : House of Lords★★, Westminster Hall★★ (hammerbeam roof★★★
Robing Room★, Central Lobby★, House of Commons★, Big Ben★, Victoria Tower★ p. 26 LY
Tower of London★★★ (Crown Jewels★★★, White Tower or Keep★★★, St. John's Chapel★
Beauchamp Tower★) p. 27 PVX.

Banqueting House★★ p. 26 LX – Buckingham Palace★★ (Changing of the Guard★★, Roy
Mews★★) p. 32 BVX – Kensington Palace★★ p. 24 FX – Lincoln's Inn★★ p. 33 EV – Lond
Bridge★ p. 27 PVX – Royal Hospital Chelsea★★ p. 31 FU – St. James's Palace★★ p. 29 EP – Sou
Bank Arts Centre ★★ (Royal Festival Hall★, National Theatre★, County Hall★) p. 26 MX – T
Temple★★ (Middle Temple Hall★) p. 22 MV – Tower Bridge★★ p. 27 PX.

Albert Memorial★ p. 30 CQ – Apsley House★ p. 28 BP – Burlington House★ p. 29 EM – Charte
house★ p. 23 NOU – Commonwealth Institute★ p. 24 EY – Design Centre★ p. 29 FM – Geor
Inn★, Southwark p. 27 PX – Gray's Inn★ p. 22 MU – Guildhall★ (Lord Mayor's Show★★) p. 23 (
– Imperial College of Science and Technology★ p. 30 CR – Dr Johnson's House★ p. 23 NUV A
Lancaster House★ p. 29 EP – Leighton House★ p. 24 EY – Linley Sambourne House★ p. 24 E'
Mansion House★ (plate and insignia★★) p. 23 PV P – The Monument★ (✳★) p. 23 PV G – C
Admiralty★ p. 26 KLX – Royal Exchange★ p. 23 PV V – Royal Opera Arcade★ (New Zeala
House) p. 29 FGN – Royal Opera House★ (Covent Garden) p. 33 DX – Somerset Hous
p. 33 EXY – Staple Inn★ p. 22 MU Y – Stock Exchange★ p. 23 PUV – Theatre Royal★ (Haymark
p. 29 GM – Westminster Bridge★ p. 26 LY.

CHURCHES

The City Churches

St. Paul's Cathedral★★★ (Dome ≤★★★) p. 23 NOV.

St. Bartholomew the Great★★ (vessel★) p. 23 OU K – St. Dunstan-in-the-East★★ p. 23 PV F
St. Mary-at-Hill★★ (plan★, woodwork★★) p. 23 PV B – Temple Church★★ p. 22 MV.

All Hallows-by-the-Tower (font cover★, brasses★) p. 23 PV Y – Christ Church★ p. 23 OU E
St. Andrew Undershaft (monuments★) p. 23 PV A – St. Bride★ (steeple★★) p. 23 NV J
St. Clement Eastcheap (panelled interior★★) p. 23 PV E – St. Edmund the King and Martyr (tow
and spire★) p. 23 PV D – St-Giles Cripplegate★ p. 23 OU N – St. Helen Bishopsgate★ (mor
ments★★) p. 23 PUV R – St. James Garlickhythe (tower and spire★, sword rests★) p. 23 OV F
St. Katherine Cree (sword rest★) p. 23 PV J – St. Magnus the Martyr (tower★, sword rest
p. 23 PV K – St. Margaret Lothbury★ (tower and spire★, woodwork★, screen★, font★) p.
PU S – St. Margaret Pattens (woodwork★) p. 23 PV N – St. Martin Ludgate (tower and spire
door cases★) p. 23 NOV B – St. Mary Abchurch★ (tower and spire★, dome★, reredos★) p.
PV X – St. Mary-le-Bow (tower and steeple★★) p. 23 OV G – St. Michael Paternoster Ro
(tower and spire★) p. 23 OV D – St. Nicholas Cole Abbey (tower and spire★) p. 23 OV F – :
Olave★ p. 23 PV S – St. Peter upon Cornhill (screen★) p. 23 PV L – St. Stephen Walbroo
(tower and steeple★, dome★), p. 23 PV Z – St. Vedast (tower and spire★, ceiling★), p.
OU E.

Other Churches

Westminster Abbey★★★ (Henry VII Chapel★★★, Chapel of Edward the Confessor★★, Chap
House★★) p. 26 LY.

Southwark Cathedral★★ p. 27 PX.

Queen's Chapel★ p. 29 EP – St Clement Danes★ p. 33 EX – St. James's★ p. 29 EM
St. Margaret's★ p. 26 LY A – St. Martin-in-the-Fields★ p. 33 DY – St. Paul's★ (Covent Garde
p. 33 DX – Westminster Roman Catholic Cathedral★ p. 26 KY B.

PARKS

Regent's Park★★★ p. 21 HI (terraces★★), Zoo★★★.

Hyde Park★★ p. 25 GHV X – St. James's Park★★ p. 26 KXY.

Kensington Gardens★ pp. 20-21 FGX (Orangery★ A).

STREETS AND SQUARES

MUSEUMS

OUTER LONDON

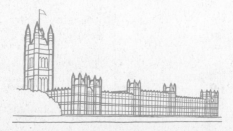

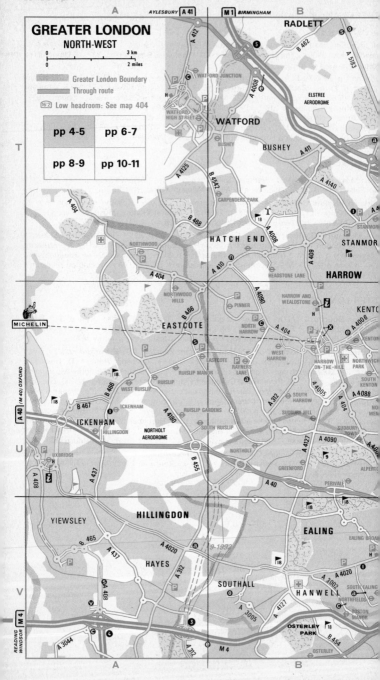

GREATER LONDON
NORTH-WEST

3 km
2 miles

Greater London Boundary
Through route

16:2 Low headroom: See map 404

| pp 4-5 | pp 6-7 |
| pp 8-9 | pp 10-11 |

C A1 GRANTHAM, BEDFORD D E

A 1000

A 1005

OREHAMWOOD

HADLEY WOOD

COCKFOSTERS

A 111

A 1081

COCKFOSTERS

18

HIGH BARNET

A5135

A 411

OAKWOOD

HIGH BARNET

A 110

A 1000

SOUTHGATE

T

M1

18

A 5109

TOTTERIDGE AND
WHETSTONE

A 41

ARNOS GROVE

NORTH FINCHLEY

A 1004

M1

A 1

A 5100

A 5109

BARNET

WOODSIDE PARK

A 1003

Circular

Road

A 105

MILL HILL

18

WEST FINCHLEY

BOUNDS GREEN

EDGWARE

MILL HILL EAST

NS PARK

A 5

18

WOOD GREEN

BURNT OAK

HENDON

FINCHLEY
CENTRAL

North

A 406

A 1000

COLINDALE

M

A 5150

A 4006

QUEENSBURY

H

A 598

EAST FINCHLEY

HORNSEY

2

KINGSBURY

HENDON
CENTRAL

V

A 1

HARINGEY

40

ESTON ROAD

C

BRENT
CROSS

UPPER
HOLLOWAY

BRENT

GOLDERS GREEN

9

HAMPSTEAD

ARCHWAY

A 400

ISLINGTON

U

WEMBLEY PARK

CHILD'S
HILL

A 502

CAMDEN

TUFNELL PARK

A 1

H

HAMPSTEAD

HOLLOWAY
ROAD

FERENCE
ENTRE

2

WEMBLEY

A 5

FINCHLEY
ROAD

BELSIZE
PARK

KENTISH
TOWN

CALEDONIAN ROAD

NEASDEN

DOLLIS HILL

WILLESDEN GREEN

A 406

KILBURN

WEST
HAMPSTEAD

ABLEY
TRAIL

A 404

TONEBRIDGE
PARK

KILBURN

HARLESDEN

WILLESDEN JUNCTION

HANGER LANE

NORTH
ACTON

LONDON CENTRE
See pp. 20 to 27

PARK ROYAL

HAMMERSMITH
AND FULHAM

WEST ACTON

EAST ACTON

LATIMER ROAD

V

NORTH
EALING

A 40

M 41

SHEPHERD'S BUSH

EALING COMMON

A 4020

GOLDHAWK RD

ACTON TOWN

A 402

STAMFORD
BROOK

S

V

CHISWICK
PARK

TURNHAM
GREEN

HAMMERSMITH

A 315

RAVENSCOURT PARK

H

GUNNERSBURY

HAMMERSMITH

A 4

D

MALL

CHISWICK

C D E

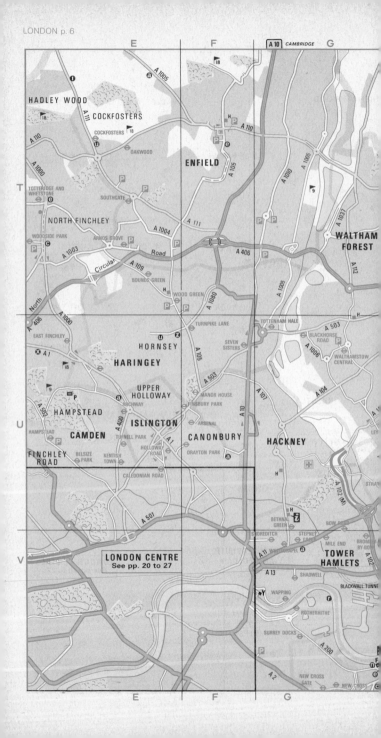

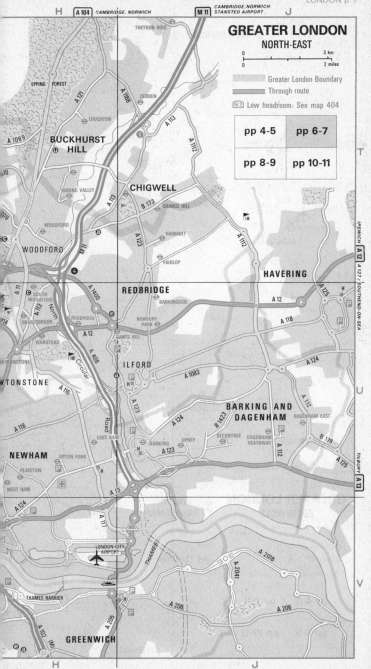

GREATER LONDON
NORTH-EAST

	3 km
0	
0	2 miles

Greater London Boundary
Through route

16·2 Low headroom: See map 404

pp 4-5	pp 6-7
pp 8-9	pp 10-11

A 104 CAMBRIDGE, NORWICH

M 11 CAMBRIDGE, NORWICH
STANSTED AIRPORT

THEYDON BOIS

EPPING FOREST

DEBDEN

A 121

A 1168

LOUGHTON

A 1069

A 113

BUCKHURST HILL

A 1112

RODING VALLEY

CHIGWELL

B 173

GRANGE HILL

A 113

WOODFORD

HAINAULT

A 123

WOODFORD

M 11

FAIRLOP

A 1112

HAVERING

A 11

A 1400

REDBRIDGE

BARKINGSIDE

A 12

A 125

SOUTH WOODFORD

North

A 113

REDBRIDGE

NEWBURY PARK

A 118

SNARESBROOK

A 12

GANTS HILL

WANSTEAD

A 406

ILFORD

A 1083

A 124

BARKING AND DAGENHAM

DAGENHAM EAST

WTONSTONE

A 116

Circular

A 123

A 124

B 1423

BECONTREE

DAGENHAM HEATHWAY

A 112

B 178

A 118

Road

A 112

A 125

EAST HAM

BARKING

UPNEY

A 123

TILBURY

NEWHAM

UPTON PARK

A 13

PLAISTOW

WEST HAM

A 124

A 13

A 117

LONDON CITY AIRPORT

A 2016

THAMES

A 2041

A 206

THAMES BARRIER

A 206

A 205

A 102 (M)

GREENWICH

IPSWICH A 12

A 127 SOUTHEND-ON-SEA

TILBURY A 13

H

J

T

C

9

U

V

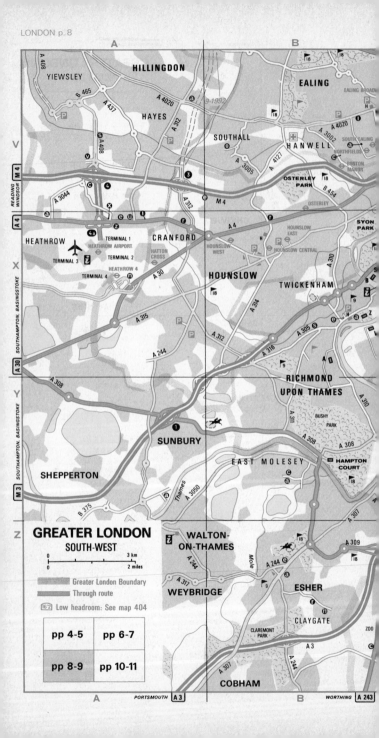

GREATER LONDON
SOUTH-WEST

0   3 km
0   2 miles

Greater London Boundary
Through route
16·2 Low headroom: See map 404

pp 4-5	pp 6-7
pp 8-9	pp 10-11

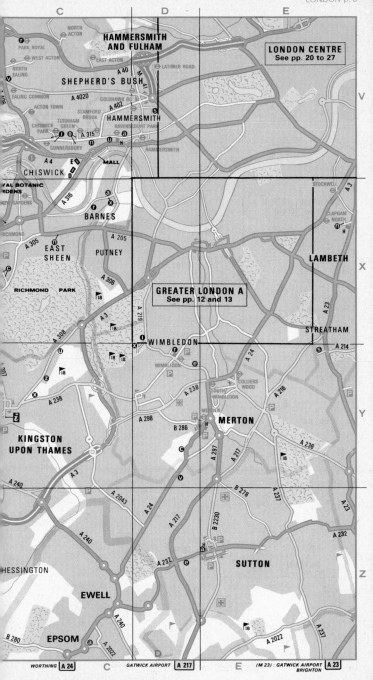

C D E

NORTH ACTON
HAMMERSMITH AND FULHAM

LONDON CENTRE
See pp. 20 to 27

PARK ROYAL
WEST ACTON
EAST ACTON
LATIMER ROAD
A 40
NORTH EALING
A 4020
SHEPHERD'S BUSH
M 41
EALING COMMON
ACTON TOWN
GOLDHAWK RD
A 402
STAMFORD BROOK
HAMMERSMITH
CHISWICK PARK
TURNHAM GREEN
A 315
RAVENSCOURT PARK
HAMMERSMITH
GUNNERSBURY
A 4
CHISWICK
MALL

ROYAL BOTANIC GARDENS
KEW GARDENS
A 316
BARNES

RICHMOND
A 305
EAST SHEEN
PUTNEY
A 205

STOCKWELL
A 3
CLAPHAM NORTH
LAMBETH

RICHMOND PARK
A 306
18

GREATER LONDON A
See pp. 12 and 13

A 3
A 219
18
STREATHAM
A 23

A 308
18
WIMBLEDON
18 18
A 214

WIMBLEDON
A 24
S
COLLIERS WOOD
A 216
SOUTH WIMBLEDON
A 238
Z
A 238
MORDEN
MERTON
A 238
18
A 236
A 298
B 286
A 297
A 217

KINGSTON UPON THAMES
A 3
B 278
A 237
A 240
A 2043
A 24
A 217
B 2230
A 23
A 232
A 240
A 232
A 2022

HESSINGTON
A 232
SUTTON
18

EWELL
A 240
A 237
A 2022
B 280
EPSOM
A 2022

V

X

Y

Z

WORTHING **A 24** | GATWICK AIRPORT **A 217** | (M 23) : GATWICK AIRPORT BRIGHTON **A 23**

C D E

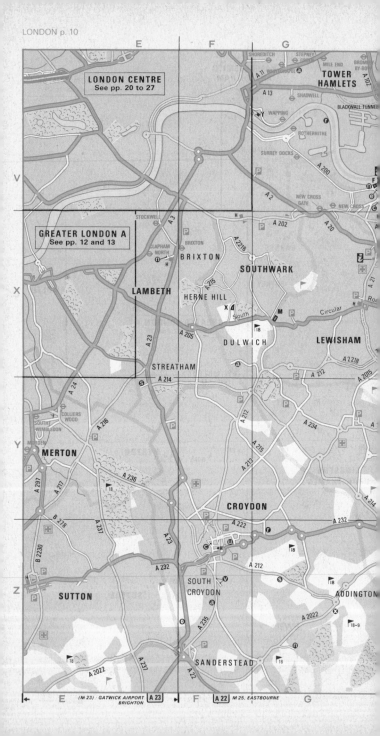

LONDON CENTRE
See pp. 20 to 27

GREATER LONDON A
See pp. 12 and 13

TOWER
HAMLETS

SOUTHWARK

LAMBETH

BRIXTON

HERNE HILL

LEWISHAM

DULWICH

STREATHAM

MERTON

CROYDON

SUTTON

SOUTH
CROYDON

ADDINGTON

SANDERSTEAD

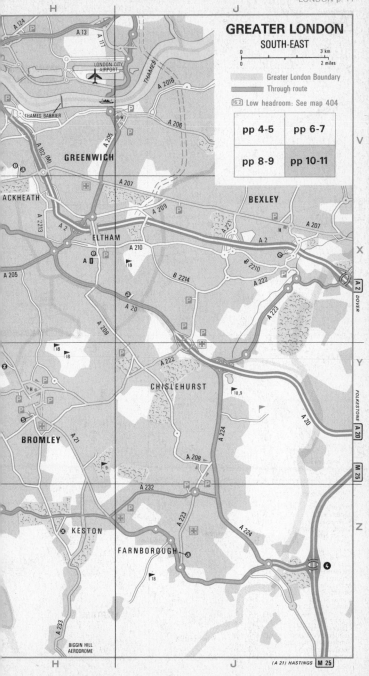

GREATER LONDON
SOUTH-EAST

0   3 km
0   2 miles

Greater London Boundary
Through route

16'2 Low headroom: See map 404

| pp 4-5 | pp 6-7 |
| pp 8-9 | pp 10-11 |

A 124
A 13
A 111
LONDON CITY AIRPORT
THAMES
A 2016
P
THAMES BARRIER
A 206
A 205
A 102 (M)
GREENWICH
A 207
ACKHEATH
A 2213
A 2
ELTHAM
A 210
BEXLEY
A 221
A 207
A 2
A 205
B 2214
A 222
B 2210
A 20
A 208
A 223
CHISLEHURST
A 222
18,9
A 20
BROMLEY
A 21
A 224
A 208
KESTON
A 232
A 223
A 224
FARNBOROUGH
A 233
BIGGIN HILL AERODROME

V

X

A 2 DOVER

Y

FOLKESTONE A 20

M 25

Z

4

H   J   (A 21) HASTINGS   M 25

A

FULHAM

HAMMERSMITH
AND FULHAM

PARSONS GREEN

BISHOP'S
PARK

PUTNEY
BRIDGE

THAMES

POL

Upper

Richmond

PUTNEY

EAST PUTNEY

Putney Bridge

West Hill

WANDSWOR

ARNDALE
SHOPPING CENTRE

H

West Hill

Park Road

Merton Road

Garratt Lane

Tibbet's Ride

SOUTHFIELDS

WIMBLEDON COMMON

Wimbledon Park Road

Durnsford Road

POL

WIMBLEDON
TENNIS

WIMBLEDON
PARK

WIMBLEDON PARK

MERTON

WIMBLEDON

Church Rd

Arthur Rd

Leopold Rd

Gap Road

Plough

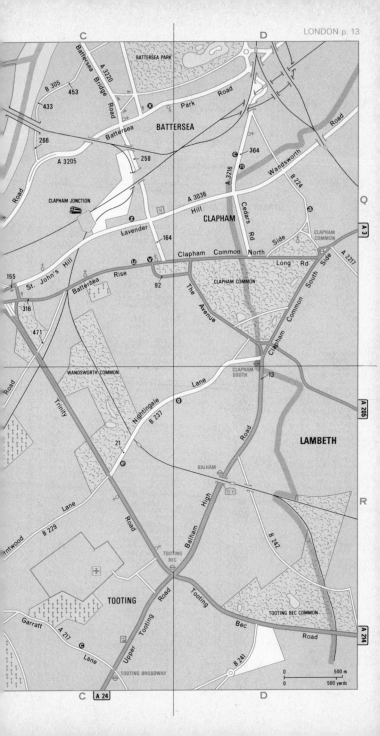

C

D

Q

A 3

A 205

R

A 214

BATTERSEA PARK

B 305
453
433
266
A 3205
A 3220
Battersea Bridge Road
Battersea
258
Park
Road

BATTERSEA

Road

CLAPHAM JONCTION

A 3036
Hill

CLAPHAM

Lavender
164

364
Wandsworth
Road
A 3216
B 224
Cedars Rd
Side

CLAPHAM COMMON

St. John's Hill
Battersea
Rise
92
Clapham
Common
North
Long
Rd
Clapham Common South Side
A 2217

155
316
471

Road

Trinity

WANDSWORTH COMMON

The
Avenue

CLAPHAM COMMON

Lane

CLAPHAM SOUTH
13

Nightingale
B 237
21

LAMBETH

Road

BALHAM
15 6

Lane
B 229
Tntwood

Road

Balham
High

B 242

TOOTING BEC

Road

TOOTING

Garratt
A 217
Lane

P

Upper Tooting
Road

Tooting

Bec
Road

TOOTING BEC COMMON

B 241

TOOTING BROADWAY

0   500 m
0   500 yards

C

A 24

D

LONDON CENTRE

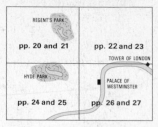

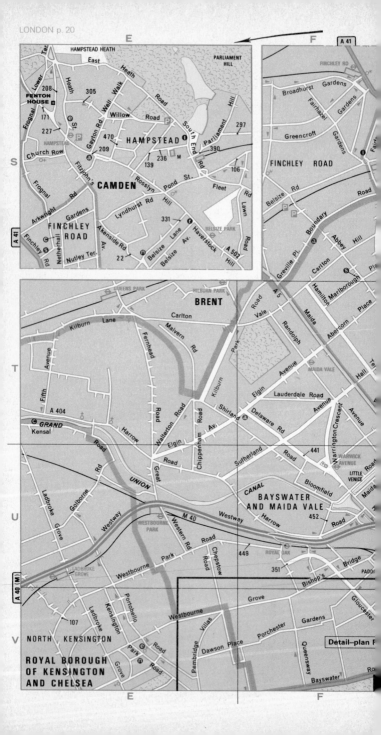

Detail—plan P

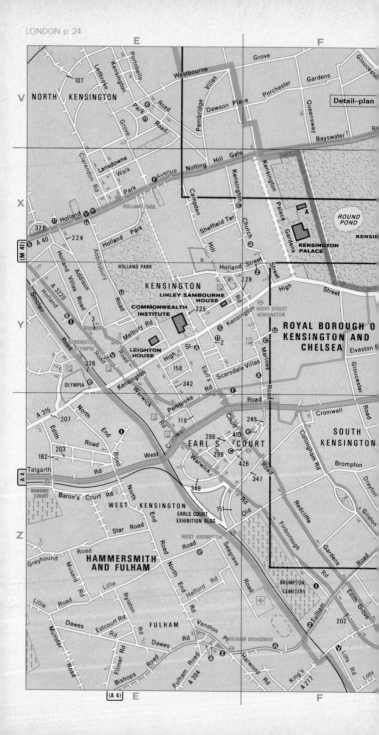

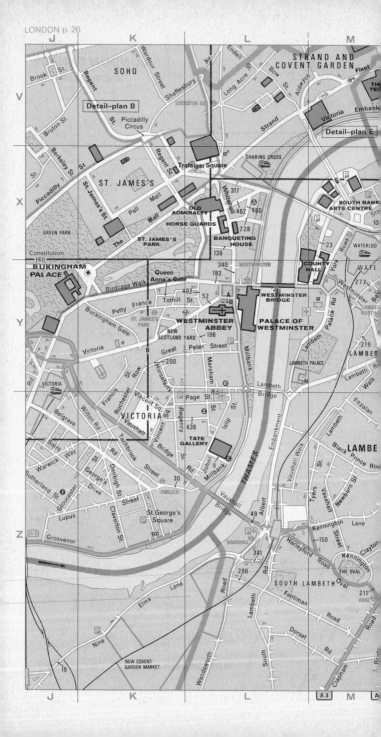

LONDON CENTRE

SOUTH-EAST

| 0 | 300 m |
| 0 | 300 yards |

N O P

ST. PAUL'S CATHEDRAL

Cheapside 352

BANK OF ENGLAND 357

BANK

318 B

304 Cannon St.

301

Queen Victoria

MANSION HOUSE

431

CITY OF LONDON

BLACKFRIARS

THAMES

38

395 431

CANNON STREET

MONUMENT

268

250

278

62

LONDON BRIDGE

TOWER HILL

TOWER OF LONDON

425

Sumner St.

Southwark Street

Great Street

Blackfriars

Road

SOUTHWARK CATHEDRAL

Tooley St.

TOWER BRIDGE

Cut

Union

Webber Street

Suffolk

Bridge

St.

High

Street

Borough

GEORGE INN

Newcomen St.

386

St. Thomas' St.

LONDON BRIDGE

Druid St.

A 200

BOROUGH

408

Long

Lane

Bermondsey Street

125

Borough Road

Trinity Church Square

POL

307

Merrick Square

St.

Trinity St.

Great Dover Street

349

Weston

Street

Grange

Abbey St.

Borough Road

Southwark

Harper Rd

SOUTHWARK

London Road

173

George's Road

R Rd

Elephant and Castle

New Kent Road

Falmouth Rd

Tower Bridge Road

Page's Walk

Willow Walk

Spa Rd

H

Grange Road

IMPERIAL WAR MUSEUM

Drive

Lane

129

306

163

Heygate St.

Rodney Rd

WALWORTH

Old

Kent

Road

Dunton

A 2

Park Road

Penton Pl.

Manor

Wakworth

Road

Flint St.

East

St.

Kent

Braganza St.

East

Street

Thurlow

St.

Road

KENNINGTON

Chapter Rd

St.

Portland

St.

Trafalgar

Z

Ruskin

Camberwell

John

Camberwell

New

Wyndham Rd

A 202

Road

Albany

Rd

Wells

Neate

St.

New Church Rd

Way

Southampton Way

Av.

B

Dorset St.
Baker
Manchester
Aybrook St.
New
Cavendish
St.
Harley
Street
Portland
Pl.

Gloucester
Blandford
St.
St.
287
Welbeck
Wimpole
Chandos
Street

Montagu
Square
Place
**WALLACE
COLLECTION**
413
Queen
Anne
St.
**REGENT'S PARK
AND MARYLEBONE**

George
Street
281
Street
Street
Cavendish
Sq.

Portman
Square
Wigmore
James
287
Henrietta
Holles
Pl.
St.

Seymour
St.
POL.
Orchard
Street
Street
Vere St.
New
Bond
Street

Bryanston
St.
Portman Street
188
Oxford
Duke
Street
Street
35
BOND ST.
South
Molton Street

Row
314
Weighhouse St.
175
Davies
12
St.

North
Street
35
175
Brook
Brook's Mews
Street
Street

Green
Lees Pl.
Street
Grosvenor
**CITY OF
WESTMINSTER**

149
Woods Mews
**Grosvenor
Square**
Grosvenor

Upper Brook
Culross
St.
St.
Carlos
Mount Row
Bruton

Upper
Grosvenor
St.
Adam's Row
Mount
St.
MAYFAIR
**Berkeley
Square**

Reeves Mews
Mount
South
Farm
St.

Aldford St.
Street
Charles Street
Curzon
Bolton

South Street
Audley
Hill
Waverton St.
Hay's
Mews
St.

132
Street
Street
Half
Moon St.

HYDE PARK
421
Curzon
**Shepherd
Market**

HYDE PARK AND KNIGHTSBRIDGE
Shepherd
Street

Serpentine
Road
220
Brick
Street

205
Old Park Lane
Piccadilly
GREEN PARK

Park
Lane

MARBLE ARCH

0   200 m
0   200 yards

**APSLEY HOUSE
WELLINGTON MUSEUM**

A   B   C

H   J   K   L   M   N   P

Oxford Street is closed to private traffic, Mondays to Saturdays : from 7 am to 7 pm between Portman Street and St. Giles Circus

C

HYDE PARK AND KNIGHTSBRIDGE

KENSINGTON GARDENS

ALBERT MEMORIAL

ROYAL ALBERT HALL

Kensington Gore

Kensington Road

Prince Consort Rd

ROYAL COLLEGE OF MUSIC

IMPERIAL COLLEGE OF SCIENCE AND

TECHNOLOGY SCIENCE MUSEUM

ROYAL COLLEGE OF ART

GEOLOGICAL MUSEUM

NATURAL HISTORY MUSEUM

Exhibition

High St

Young St

Kensington Square

KENSINGTON

St. Alban's Grove

De Vere Gardens

Palace Gate

Victoria Rd

Victoria Grove

Gloucester

Queen's Gate Terrace

Elvaston Place

Queen's Gate

Cornwall Gardens

Lexham Gardens

Lexham Gdns

Grenville Place

Gate Gardens

Gardens

Cromwell Road

Cromwell Road

Knaresborough Place

Courtfield Gdns

Courtfield Gdns

Courtfield Place

Harrington Gardens

Ashburn Road

Stanhope Gardens

GLOUCESTER RD

Queen's Gate

SOUTH KENSINGTON

Bramham Gdns

Bolton Gardens

Wetherby Gardens

Bina Gdns

Old Brompton Road

Drayton Gardens

Roland Gardens

Onslow Gardens

Cranley Gdns

Onslow Gdns

Onslow Square

Summer Square

Fulham

Earl's Court Rd

Brompton

Old Brompton Rd

EARL'S COURT

The Boltons

Little Boltons

Gilston Road

Evelyn Gdns

Elm Park Rd

Elm Park Gdns

Beaufort

Elm Park Road

The Vale

Old

Redcliffe Square

Finborough Road

Redcliffe Gardens

Ifield Road

Harcourt Ter

Tregunter Road

Hollywood Road

Fulham Road

Park Walk

Elm Street

South P.

BROMPTON CEMETERY

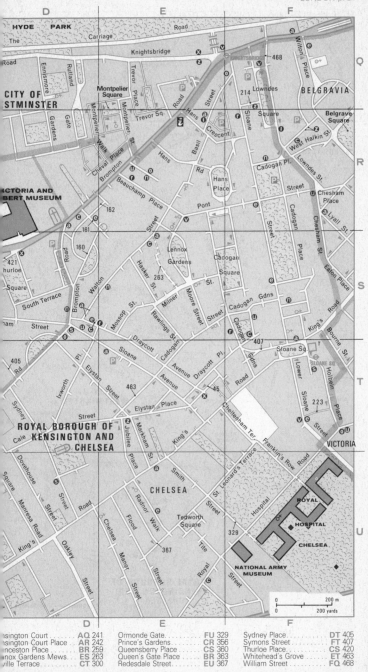

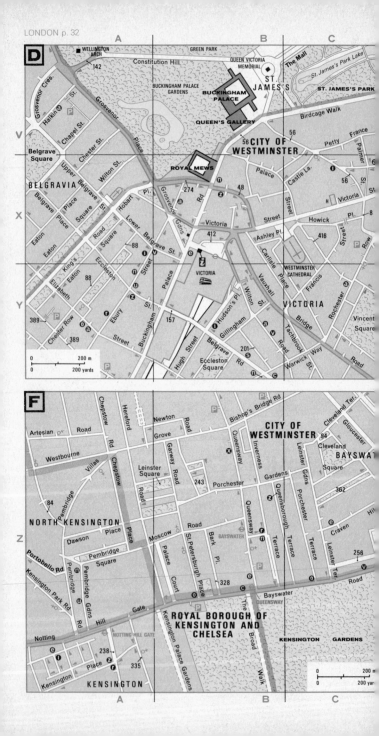

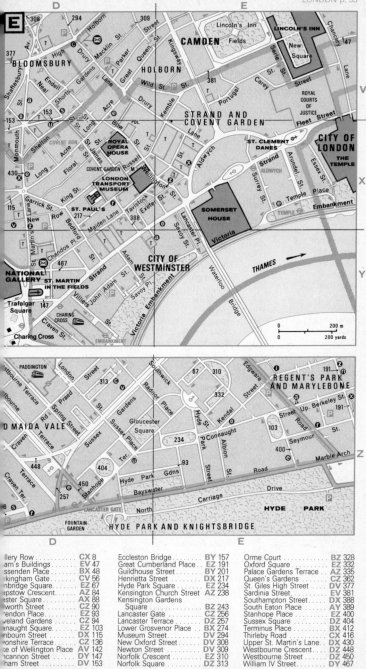

Alphabetical list of hotels and restaurants
Liste alphabétique des hôtels et restaurants
Elenco alfabetico degli alberghi e ristoranti
Alphabetisches Hotel- und Restaurantverzeichnis

Alphabetical list of areas included
Liste alphabétique des quartiers cités
Elenco alfabetico dei quartieri citati
Liste der erwähnten Bezirke

Starred establishments in London
Les établissements à étoiles de Londres
Gli esercizi con stelle a Londra
Die Stern-Restaurants Londons

	Area	Page
XXXX **Le Gavroche**	Mayfair	70

	Area	Page
XXXX **La Tante Claire**	Chelsea	59
XXXX **Chez Nico**	Regents Park and Marylebone	72
XXX **Harvey's**	Wandsworth	67

❀

	Area	Page			Area	Page
Connaught	Mayfair	69	XXX **Arlequin (L')**	Battersea	67
Capital	Chelsea	58	XXX **Suntory**	St. James's	73
XXX **Oak Room**	Mayfair	70	XXX **Tatsuso**	City	52
XXX **Four Seasons**	Mayfair	70	XX **Sutherlands**	Soho	74

Further establishments which merit your attention
Autres tables qui méritent votre attention
Altre tavole particolarmente interessanti
Weitere empfehlenswerte Häuser

M

		Page				Page
XX **Al Bustan**	Belgravia	68	XXX **Zen Central**	Mayfair	70
XX **Bibendum**	Chelsea	59	XX **Le Caprice**	St. James's	74
XX **Chutney Mary**	Chelsea	59	XX **Hilaire**	South Kensington	63
XX **Dynasty II**	Chelsea	59	XX **Simply Nico**	Victoria	76
XX **Now and Zen**	Strand and Covent Garden	75	X **Vijay**	Kilburn	49
XX **Red Fort**	Soho	74	X **Chinon**	Shepherd's Bush	55
XX **Turner's**	Chelsea	59	X **Kensington Place**	Kensington	61

Restaurants classified according to type
Restaurants classés suivant leur genre
Ristoranti classificati secondo il loro genere
Restaurants nach Art und Einrichtung geordnet

Bistro

X **Bangkok** (Royal Borough of Kensington - *South Kensington*) 64

X **Bougie (La)** (Camden - *Camden Town*) 51

X **Langan's Bistro** (City of Westminster - *Regent's Park & Marylebone*) 7

Seafood

XX **Gravier** (Kingston-upon-Thames - *Kingston*) 64

XX **Hippocampe (L')** (City of Westminster - *Soho*) 74

XX **Lucullus** (Westminster - *Hyde Park*) 69

XX **Poissonnerie de l'Avenue** (Royal Borough of Kensington & Chelsea - *Chelsea*) 59

XX **Seppia (La)** (City of Westminster - *Mayfair*) 71

XX **Sheekey's** (City of Westminster - *Strand & Covent Garden*) 7

XX **Suquet (Le)** (Royal Borough of Kensington & Chelsea - *Chelsea*) 6

XX **Tiger Lee** (Royal Borough of Kensington & Chelsea - *Chelsea*) 6

X **34 Surrey Street** (Croydon - *Croydon*) 5

Californian

XX **34 Surrey Street** (Croydon - *Croydon*) 5

Chinese

XXXX **Oriental** (Westminster - *Mayfair*).. 70

XXX **Empress Garden** (City of Westminster - *Mayfair*) 70

XXX **Inn of Happiness** (City of Westminster - *Victoria*) 76

XXX **Now and Zen** (Westminster - *Strand and Covent Garden*) 75

XXX **Princess Garden** (City of Westminster - *Mayfair*) 70

XXX **Zen** (Royal Borough of Kensington & Chelsea - *Chelsea*) 59

XXX **Zen Central** (City of Westminster - *Mayfair*) 70

XX **Bayee Village** (Merton - *Wimbledon*) 65

XX **China Jazz** (Camden - *Regent's Park*) 52

XX **Chin's** (Hammersmith - *Fulham*).. 5

XX **Dragon City** (Redbridge - *Ilford*) .. 6

XX **Four Regions** (Richmond - *Richmond*) 6

XX **Gallery Rendezvous** (City of Westminster - *Soho*) 7

XX **Good Earth** (Barnet - *Mill Hill*) 4

XX **Good Earth** (Royal Borough of Kensington & Chelsea - *Chelsea*) 6

XX **Grove Park** (Hounslow - *Chiswick*) 5

XX **Hee's** (Hounslow - *Hounslow*).... 5

XX **Ho-Ho** (Redbridge - *South Woodford*) 6

XX **Hsing** (City of Westminster - *Bayswater & Maida Vale*) 6

Chinese

English

French

French

Hungarian

Indian & Pakistan

Italian

XX **L'Incontro** (City of Westminster - *Victoria*) 76

XX **Santini** (City of Westminster - *Victoria*) 76

XX **Amico (L')** (City of Westminster - *Victoria*) 76

XX **Antonio's** (Hounslow - *Chiswick*) . . 57

XX **Beccofino** (Royal Borough of Kensington & Chelsea - *Chelsea*) 60

XX **Dell Arte** (Westminster - *Hyde Park*) 69

XX **Eleven Park Walk** (Royal Borough of Kensington & Chelsea - *Chelsea*) 59

XX **Fenice (La)** (Kensington - *Kensington*) 61

XX **Finezza (La)** (Royal Borough of Kensington & Chelsea - *Chelsea*) . 59

XX **Fontana Amorosa** (City of Westminster - *Regent's Park & Marylebone*) 73

XX **Giannino's** (Bromley - *Keston*) 50

XX **Gran Paradiso** (City of Westminster - *Victoria*) 76

XX **Gritti** (Westminster - *Strand & Covent Garden*) 75

XX **Loggia (La)** (City of Westminster - *Regent's Park & Marylebone*) 73

XX **Luigi's** (Southwark - *Dulwich*) 66

XX **Mezzaluna** (Barnet - *Child's Hill*) . . 49

XX **Orso** (City of Westminster - *Strand & Covent Garden*) 75

XX **Paesana (La)** (Royal Borough of Kensington & Chelsea - *Kensington*) 61

XX **Primula (La)** (Royal Borough of Kensington & Chelsea - *Earl's Court*) 60

XX **Salotto** (Ealing - *Ealing*) 53

XX **Salotto** (Royal Borough of Kensington & Chelsea - *Chelsea*) 59

XX **Sandrini** (Kensington - *Chelsea*) . . 59

XX **San Marino** (City of Westminster - *Bayswater & Maida Vale*) 68

XX **Seppia (La)** (City of Westminster - *Mayfair*) 71

XX **Toto's** (Royal Borough of Kensington & Chelsea - *Chelsea*) 60

X **Barbino (Il)** (City of Westminster - *Regent's Park & Marylebone*) 73

X **Capisano** (Bromley - *Bromley*) 50

X **Castelletto (Il)** (Camden - *Bloomsbury*) 51

X **Cibo** (Royal Borough of Kensington & Chelsea - *Kensington*) 61

X **Fontana (La)** (City of Westminster - *Victoria*) 76

X **Formula Veneta** (Royal Borough of Kensington & Chelsea - *Earl's Court*) 60

X **Laguna** (City of Westminster - *Strand & Covent Garden*) 75

X **Mario** (Croydon - *Croydon*) 53

X **Mimmo d'Ischia** (City of Westminster - *Victoria*) 76

X **Paolo's** (Ealing - *Ealing*) 53

X **Riva** (Richmond - *Barnes*) 65

X **Roberto's** (Hillingdon - *Ickenham*) . 57

X **Sambuca** (Hillingdon - *Eastcote*) . . 56

X **San Vincenzo (Al)** (Westminster - *Bayswater*) 68

X **Trattoria Sorrentina** (Harrow - *Central*) 55

X **Villa Medici** (City of Westminster - *Victoria*) 76

X **Ziani** (Royal Borough of Kensington & Chelsea - *Chelsea*) 60

Japanese

XXX **Benihana** (Camden - *Hampstead*) . 51

XXX ۞ **Suntory** (City of Westminster - *St. James's*) 73

XXX ۞**Tatsuso** (City of London) 52

XX **Asuka** (City of Westminster - *Regent's Park & Marylebone*) 73

XX **Hiroko** (Royal Borough of Kensington & Chelsea - *Kensington*) 61

XX **Hot Gossip** (Hammersmith - *Fulham*) 55

XX **Masako** (City of Westminster - *Regent's Park & Marylebone*) 72

XX **Miyama** (City of London) 52

XX **Miyama** (City of Westminster - *Mayfair*) 69

XX **Mon** (City of Westminster - *Regent's Park & Marylebone*) 72

XX **Nakano** (Royal Borough of Kensington & Chelsea - *Chelsea*) 59

XX **Shogun** (City of Westminster - *Mayfair*) 71

X **Ikeda** (City of Westminster - *Mayfair*) 71

X **Imari** (Camden - *Holborn*) 52

X **Koto** (Camden - *Regents Park*) 52

X **Nakamura** (City of Westminster - *Regent's Park & Marylebone*) 73

X **Neshiko** (Islington - *Islington*) 58

Korean

Lebanese

Oriental

Polish

Swedish

Thai

Vietnamese

Restaurants open on Sunday (L = lunch – D = dinner) and Restaurants taking last orders after 11.30 pm (•)

Restaurants ouverts le dimanche (L = déjeuner – D = dîner) et restaurants prenant les dernières commandes après 23 h 30 (•)

Ristoranti aperti la domenica (L = colazione – D = cena) e ristoranti che accettano ordinazioni dopo le 23.30 (•)

Restaurants, die sonntags geöffnet sind (L = Mittagessen – D = Abendessen) BZW. Bestellungen auch nach 23.00 Uhr annehmen (•)

Berkeley (Restaurant) .... L D   68
(City of Westminster - Belgravia)

Claridge's (Causerie) .... L D   69
(City of Westminster - Mayfair)

Hyatt Carlton Tower
(Chelsea Room) .... L D   58
(Rib Room) .... L D
(Royal Borough of Kensington & Chelsea - Chelsea)

Four Seasons Inn on the Park   69
(lanes 12.00) .... L D •
(City of Westminster - Mayfair)

Savoy (River) .... L D   74
(City of Westminster - Strand & Covent Garden)

Halcyon (Kingfisher) .... L D •   60
(Royal Borough of Kensington & Chelsea - Kensington)

90 Park Lane .... L D   70
(City of Westminster - Mayfair)

Chateau (Le) .... L D   70
(City of Westminster - Mayfair)

⊛ Four Seasons .... L D   70
(City of Westminster - Mayfair)

Soufflé (Le) .... L D   70
(City of Westminster - Mayfair)

Bastide (La) .... •   74
(City of Westminster - Soho)

Bibendum .... L D •   59
(Royal Borough of Kensington & Chelsea - Chelsea)

Bombay Brasserie (12.00) .... L D •   63
(Royal Borough of Kensington & Chelsea - South Kensington)

Dynasty II (1.30) .... L D •   59
(Royal Borough of Kensington & Chelsea - Chelsea)

Empress Garden .... L D   70
(City of Westminster - Mayfair)

Incontro (L') .... D •   76
(City of Westminster - Victoria)

Inn of Happiness .... L D   76
(City of Westminster - Victoria)

Ivy (12.00) .... L D •   75
(City of Westminster - Strand & Covent Garden)

Leith's .... D •   62
(Royal Borough of Kensington & Chelsea - North Kensington)

Lindsay House (12.00) .... L D •   74
(City of Westminster - Soho)

Princess Garden .... L D   61
(City of Westminster - Mayfair)

Santini .... D •   76
(City of Westminster - Victoria)

Waltons .... L D •   59
(Royal Borough of Kensington & Chelsea - Chelsea)

Zen Central .... L D •   70
(City of Westminster - Mayfair)

Spice Merchant .... L D •   68
(City of Westminster - Bayswater & Maida Vale)

Antonio's .... L D   57
(Hounslow - Chiswick)

Ayudhya .... L D   64
(Kingston - Kingston)

Bayee Village .... L D   65
(Merton - Wimbledon)

Beccofino .... •   60
(Royal Borough of Kensington & Chelsea - Chelsea)

Bengal Lancer (12.00) .... L D •   52
(Camden - Kentish Town)

Blue Elephant (12.30) .... L D •   55
(Hammersmisth - Fulham)

Boyd's .... L D   61
(Royal Borough of Kensington & Chelsea - Kensington)

Busabong Too .... L D   59
(Royal Borough of Kensington & Chelsea - Chelsea)

Caprice (Le) (12.00) .... L D •   74
(City of Westminster - St. James's)

Carapace L   51
(Camden - Hampstead)

Chin's .... L D •   55
(Hammersmith - Fulham)

Chow Shing (12.00) .... L D •   57
(Hounslow - Chiswick)

※	Shanghai ....L D (Royal Borough of Kensington & Chelsea - *Kensington*)	61
※	Shogun....................D (City of Westminster - *Mayfair*)	71
※	Soong....................L D (Camden - *Hampstead*)	51
※	Sonny's ....L (Richmond-upon-Thames - *Barnes*)	65
※	Suquet (Le) ....L D ● (Royal Borough of Kensington & Chelsea - *Chelsea*)	60
※	Tandoori Nights (12.00) ......L D ● (Hammersmith - *Hammersmith*)	55
※	Thirty-Four Surrey Street .... L (Croydon - *Croydon*)	53
※	Thurlows ....L (Richmond - *Barnes*)	65
※	Tino's....................L D (City of Westminster - *Regent's Park & Marylebone*)	73
※	Toto's....................L D ● (Royal Borough of Kensington & Chelsea - *Chelsea*)	60
※	Treasure of China ....L D ● (Greenwich - *Greenwich*)	54
※	Tui ....L D (Royal Borough of Kensing- ton & Chelsea - *South Kensing- ton*)	63
※※	Willow ....L D (Croydon - *Addington*)	52
※※	Xian ....D (Bromley - *Farnborough*)	50
※※	Zai'qa Tandoori ....L D (Barnet - *High Barnet*)	49
※※	Zen W3....................L D ● (Camden - *Hampstead*)	51
※	Annapurna (12.00) ....L D ● (Hounslow - *Chiswick*)	57
※	Ark (The) ....D (Royal Borough of Kensington & Chelsea - *Kensington*)	62
※	Barbino (II) (11.45) ....● (City of Westminster - *Regent's Park & Marylebone*)	73
※	Bois St. Jean (Au) ....L D ● (City of Westminster - *Regent's Park & Marylebone*)	73
※	Bombay Bicycle Club ....● (Wandsworth - *Wandsworth*)	67
※	Bougie (La)................L D ● (Camden - *Camden Town*)	51
※	Brilliant....................D (Ealing - *Southall*)	53
※	Café Kensington ....L D ● (Royal Borough of Kensington & Chelsea - *Kensington*)	61
※	Chanterelle................L D ● (Kensington - *South Kensington*)	64

※	Chateaubriand (12.00) ....● (Camden - *Hampstead*)	61
※	Cibo ....L (Royal Borough of Kensington & Chelsea - *Kensington*)	
※	Dordogne (La) ....D (Hounslow - *Chiswick*)	57
※	Fontana (La)................L D (City of Westminster - *Victoria*)	76
※	Fortune Cookie ....L D (City of Westminster - *Bayswater & Maida Vale*)	68
※	Fung Shing................L D ● (City of Westminster - *Soho*)	74
※	Garden ....L D (Hammersmith & Fulham - *Ham- mersmith*)	55
※	Happiness Garden..........D ● (Ealing - *Hanwell*)	53
※	Jashan ....L D ● (Haringey - *Hornsey*)	55
※	Jasmin ....L D ● (Wandsworth - *Clapham*)	67
※	Kensington Place (11.45) .....L D ● (Royal Borough of Kensington & Chelsea - *Kensington*)	61
※	Left Bank ....L ● (Royal Borough of Kensington & Chelsea - *Kensington*)	60
※	Magno's Brasserie ....● (City of Westminster - *Strand & Covent Garden*)	75
※	Malabar ....L D (Royal Borough of Kensington & Chelsea - *Kensington*)	61
※	Midi (Le)..................L D (Hammersmith - *Fulham*)	55
※	Mimmo d'Ischia............● (City of Westminster - *Victoria*)	76
※	Mr Tang's Mandarin ....L D (Harrow - *Stanmore*)	56
※	Nakamura..................D (City of Westminster - *Regent's Park & Marylebone*)	73
※	Nam Long at Le Shaker......● (Royal Borough of Kensington & Chelsea - *South Kensington*)	64
※	Noughts 'N' Crosses........L (Ealing - *Ealing*)	53
※	Peking Diner..................● (Bromley - *Bromley*)	50
※	Pollyanna's (12.00)..........L ● (Wandsworth - *Clapham*)	67
※	Quality Chop House ....L D ● (Islington - *Finsbury*)	57
※	Raj Vogue (11.45)..........L D ● (Islington - *Upper Holloway*)	58
※	Riva ....L D (Richmond - *Barnes*)	65
※	Saigon ....● (City of Westminster - *Soho*)	74
※	Sambuca ....L D ● (Hillingdon - *Eastcote*)	56

Boroughs and areas

reater London is divided, for administrative purposes, into 32 boroughs plus the City : these ub-divide naturally into minor areas, usually grouped around former villages or quarters, hich often maintain a distinctive character.

BARNET pp. 4 and 5.

Child's Hill – ⊠ NW2 – ☎ 071.

XX **Mezzaluna,** 424 Finchley Rd, NW2, ℰ 794 0455, Italian rest. – ⚠ 𝑉𝐼𝑆𝐴 DU o
closed Monday – **M** 15.00 **t.** (lunch) and a la carte 17.50/25.50 **t.** ⓝ 4.00.

X **Quincy's,** 675 Finchley Rd, NW2 2JP, ℰ 794 8499 – ▤. ⚠ 𝑉𝐼𝑆𝐴 DU r
closed Sunday, Monday and 24 December-30 January – **M** (booking essential) (dinner only) 22.50 **t.** ⓝ 4.50.

X **Laurent,** 428 Finchley Rd, NW2 2HY, ℰ 794 3603, Coucous – ⚠ 𝑉𝐼𝑆𝐴 DU o
closed Sunday, first 3 weeks August and Bank Holidays – **M** a la carte approx. 11.55 **t.**

Hendon – ⊠ NW4 – ☎ 081 – ⓝ off Sanders Lane ℰ 346 6023.

🏨 **Hendon Hall** (Mt. Charlotte Thistle), Ashley Lane, NW4 1HF, ℰ 203 3341, Telex 8956088, Fax 203 9709, ⌗ – ▐▌ 🆃🆅 ☎ 🅿 – ⚠ 330. ⚠ ⚠ 🅞 𝑉𝐼𝑆𝐴. ⌗ DU v
M 14.50/15.90 **st.** and a la carte ⓝ 5.10 – � 7.50 – **51 rm** ⊐ 75.00/102.00 **st.**, **1 suite** 130.00.

🏠 **Peacehaven** without rest., 94 Audley Rd, NW4 3HB, ℰ 202 9758, ⌗ – 🆃🆅. ⚠ ⚠ 🅞 𝑉𝐼𝑆𝐴. ⌗
13 rm ⊐ 38.00/66.00 **st.** CU c

High Barnet – ⊠ Herts – ☎ 081.

ⓝ Old Fold Manor, Hadley Green ℰ 440 9185 – ⓝ Arkley, Rowley Green Rd ℰ 449 0394.

XX **Zai'qa Tandoori,** 7d High St., EN5 5UE, ℰ 441 6375, Indian rest. – ⚠ ⚠ 🅞 𝑉𝐼𝑆𝐴 DT c
closed 25 December – **M** a la carte 9.35/14.25 **t.**

Mill Hill – ⊠ NW7 – ☎ 081 – ⓝ 100 Barnet Way ℰ 959 2282.

XX **Good Earth,** 143-145 The Broadway, NW7 4RN, ℰ 959 7011, Chinese rest. – ▤. ⚠ ⚠ 🅞 𝑉𝐼𝑆𝐴
M 11.50/30.00 **t.** and a la carte ⓝ 3.50. CT a

North Finchley – ⊠ NW8 – ☎ 081.

XX Xian, 862 High Rd, N12, ℰ 445 8125, Chinese rest. ET c

BEXLEY pp. 10 and 11.

Bexley – ⊠ Kent – ☎ 0322 Crayford

🏨 Forte Crest, Black Prince Interchange, Southwold Rd, DA5 1ND, on A 2 ℰ 526900, Fax 526113 – ▐▌ ⌗ rm ▤ rest 🆃🆅 ☎ & 🅿 – ⚠ 70. ⚠ ⚠ 𝑉𝐼𝑆𝐴 JX e
M (closed Saturday lunch) (carving lunch) 13.75/16.50 **st.** and a la carte ⓝ 4.95 – ⊐ 8.50 – **104 rm, 2 suites.**

BRENT pp. 4 and 5.

Kilburn – ⊠ NW6 – ☎ 071.

X **Vijay,** 49 Willesden Lane, NW6 7RF, ℰ 328 1087, South Indian rest. – ▤. ⚠ ⚠ 🅞 𝑉𝐼𝑆𝐴 DU n
M a la carte approx. 14.00 **st.**

Wembley – ⊠ Middx – ☎ 081 – ⓝ Sudbury, Bridgwater Rd ℰ 902 0218.

🏨 **Hilton National,** Empire Way, HA9 8DS, ℰ 902 8839, Telex 24837, Fax 900 2201 – ▐▌ ▤ rest 🆃🆅 ☎ 🅿 – ⚠ 300. ⚠ ⚠ 🅞 𝑉𝐼𝑆𝐴. ⌗ CU z
M (carving rest.) 16.00/17.50 **st.** and a la carte ⓝ 5.60 – ⊐ 9.25 – **300 rm** 99.00/225.00 **st.** – SB (weekends only) 124.00/136.00 **st.**

BROMLEY pp. 10 and 11.

, ⓝ Cray Valley, Sandy Lane ℰ 0689 (Orpington) 31927, NE : by A 224 – ⓝ, ⓝ Sundridge Park, arden Lane ℰ 460 1822.

Bromley – ⊠ Kent – ☎ 081 – ⓝ Magpie Hall Lane ℰ 462 7014.

🏨 **Bromley Court,** Bromley Hill, BR1 4JD, ℰ 464 5011, Telex 896310, Fax 460 0899, ⌗ – ▐▌ 🆃🆅 ☎ 🅿 – ⚠ 120. ⚠ ⚠ 🅞 𝑉𝐼𝑆𝐴 HY z
M (closed Saturday lunch) 13.75 **st.** and a la carte ⓝ 4.05 – **122 rm** ⊐ 72.00/85.00 **st.**

✗ **Capisano,** 9 Simpsons Rd, BR2 9AP, ✆ 464 8036, Italian rest. – ▣ 壓 *VISA*　　　HY
closed Saturday lunch, Sunday, 3 weeks August and Bank Holidays – **M** a la carte 13.00
18.90 **t.** ⑴ 3.80.

✗ **Peking Diner,** 71 Burnt Ash Lane, BR1 5AA, ✆ 464 7911, Chinese rest. – ▣ 壓 ◑ *VS*
closed Sunday and 25-26 December – **M** 8.00/12.50 **st.** and a la carte ⑴ 3.75.　　HX

Farnborough – ✉ Kent – ✿ 0689 Farnborough.
⛳ High Elms, High Elms Rd, Orpington ✆ 58175, off A 21 via Shire Lane.

✗✗ **Xian,** 324 High St., Orpington, BR6 0NG, ✆ 0689 (Orpington) 871881, Chinese (Peking
Szechuan) rest. – ▤. ▣ 壓 ◑ *VISA*　　JZ
closed Sunday lunch – **M** 7.20/11.20 **t.** and a la carte.

Keston – ✉ Kent – ✿ 0689 Farnborough

✗✗ **Giannino's,** 6 Commonside, BR4 2TS, ✆ 856410, Italian rest. – ▣ 壓 ◑ *VISA*　　HZ
closed Sunday and Monday – **M** 12.75/14.75 **t.** and a la carte ⑴ 4.50.

CAMDEN Except where otherwise stated see pp. 20-23.

Bloomsbury – ✉ NW1/W1/WC1 – ✿ 071 – 🛈 35-36 Woburn Pl., WC1 ✆ 580 4599.

🏨 **Russell** (Forte), Russell Sq., WC1B 5BE, ✆ 837 6470, Telex 24615, Fax 837 2857 –
🛗 ⇔ rm 📺 ☎ – 🛄 450. ▣ 壓 ◑ *VISA*　　LU
M (carving lunch) 15.50 **st.** and a la carte ⑴ 5.50 – ☑ 9.85 – **324 rm** 95.00/170.00 **st.**
3 suites 145.00/199.00. – SB (weekends only) 118.00 **st.**

🏨 **Mountbatten** (Edwardian), 20 Monmouth St., WC2H 9HD, ✆ 836 4300, Telex 29808
Fax 240 3540 – 🛗 ⇔ rm ▤ rest 📺 ☎ – 🛄 75. ▣ 壓 ◑ *VISA*　p. 33 DV
M (closed lunch Saturday, Sunday and Bank Holidays) 16.50/22.50 **st.** – ☑ 12.00 – **121 rm**
163.00/181.00 **st.**, **6 suites** 150.00/398.00 **st.**

🏨 **Marlborough** (Edwardian), Bloomsbury St., WC1B 3QD, ✆ 636 5601, Telex 29827
Fax 636 0532 – 🛗 ⇔ rm ▤ rest 📺 ☎ & – 🛄 200. ▣ 壓 ◑ *VISA*. ✎　　LU
M (closed Sunday lunch) 14.50/18.50 **st.** and a la carte ⑴ 5.00 – ☑ 10.50 – **167 rm**
120.00/167.00 **st.**, **2 suites** 200.00/385.00 **st.** – SB (weekends only) 160.00 **st.**

🏨 **Grafton** (Edwardian), 130 Tottenham Court Rd, W1P 9HP, ✆ 388 4131, Telex 29723
Fax 387 7394 – 🛗 ▤ rest 📺 ☎ – 🛄 100. ▣ 壓 ◑ *VISA*. ✎　　KU
M (closed Saturday lunch) 12.00/15.00 **st.** and a la carte ⑴ 6.50 – ☑ 10.00 – **233 rm** 119.00
180.00 **st.**, **4 suites** 230.00/250.00 **st.**

🏨 **Montague Park,** 12-20 Montague St., WC1B 5BJ, ✆ 637 1001, Telex 23307
Fax 637 2506 – 🛗 ▤ 📺 ☎ & – 🛄 80. ▣ 壓 ◑ *VISA*. ✎　　LU
M (closed lunch Saturday and Sunday) 13.50/16.50 **st.** and a la carte ⑴ 5.75 – ☑ 9.50
109 rm 91.00/157.00 **st.**

🏨 **Kenilworth** (Edwardian), 97 Great Russell St., WC1B 3LB, ✆ 637 3477, Telex 2584
Fax 631 3133 – 🛗 ▤ rest 📺 ☎ – 🛄 100. ▣ 壓 ◑ *VISA*. ✎　　LU
M 16.95 **st.** and a la carte ⑴ 5.00 – ☑ 10.00 – **191 rm** 111.00/152.00 **st.**, **1 suite** 186.00
255.00 **st.**

🏨 **Forte Crest,** Coram St., WC1N 1HT, ✆ 837 1200, Fax 837 5374 – 🛗 ⇔ rm ▤ rest 📺 ☎
🛄 700. ▣ 壓 ◑ *VISA*　　LT
M (carving lunch)/dinner 16.50 and a la carte ⑴ 9.95 – ☑ 10.25 – **281 rm** 95.00/105.00 **st.**
3 suites 250.00 **st.** – SB (weekends only) 98.00 **st.**

🏨 **Portland,** 7 Montague St., WC1B 5BP, ✆ 323 1717, Fax 636 6498 – 🛗 ▤ rest 📺 ☎. ▣
◑ *VISA*. ✎　　LU
M (closed Saturday lunch and Sunday) (Italian rest.) 13.50 **t.** and a la carte ⑴ 4.90 – **25 rm**
75.00/110.00 **st.**, **1 suite** 190.00 **st.** – SB (January. July-August and weekends) 90.00 **st.**

🏨 **Bonnington,** 92 Southampton Row, WC1B 4BH, ✆ 242 2828, Telex 26159
Fax 831 9170 – 🛗 ⇔ rm ▤ rest 📺 ☎ & – 🛄 120. ▣ 壓 ◑ *VISA*　　LU
M 15.00 **st.** and a la carte ⑴ 3.20 – **215 rm** ☑ 92.00/116.00 **st.** – SB (weekends only)
120.00/150.00 **st.**

🏨 **Kingsley** (Mt. Charlotte Thistle), Bloomsbury Way, WC1A 2SD, ✆ 242 5881, Telex 2115
Fax 831 0225 – 🛗 ▤ 📺 ☎ – 🛄 100. ▣ 壓 ◑ *VISA*. ✎　　LU
M (closed lunch Saturday, Sunday and Bank Holidays) 15.25 **t.** and a la carte ⑴ 4.55
– ☑ 8.50 – **98 rm** 69.00/79.00 **st.**, **2 suites** 225.00 **st.**

🏨 **Bloomsbury Park** (Mt. Charlotte Thistle), 126 Southampton Row, WC1B 5AD,
✆ 430 0434, Telex 25757, Fax 242 0665 – 🛗 ⇔ rm 📺 ☎ – 🛄 30. ▣ 壓 ◑ *VISA*. ✎
M (closed Friday dinner, Saturday, Sunday and Bank Holidays) (bar lunch)/dinner 13.95
and a la carte ⑴ 4.60 – ☑ 8.40 – **95 rm** 84.50/120.00 **st.**　　LU

🏨 **Academy,** 17-21 Gower St., WC1E 6HG, ✆ 631 4115, Telex 24364, Fax 636 3442 – ▤ rest
📺 ☎. ▣ 壓 ◑ *VISA*. ✎　　KLU
M 14.00/16.00 **t.** and a la carte ⑴ 4.25 – ☑ 7.95 – **33 rm** 65.00/120.00 **s.**

🏠 **Harlingford** without rest., 61-63 Cartwright Gdns, WC1H 9EL, ✆ 387 1551, Fax 387 4616
✎ – 📺 ☎. ▣ *VISA*. ✎ – **43 rm** ☑ 42.00/54.00 **st.**　　LT

🏠 **Mabledon Court** without rest., 10-11 Mabledon Pl., WC1H 9BA, ✆ 388 3866
Fax 387 5686 – 🛗 📺 ☎. ▣ *VISA*. ✎
33 rm ☑ 45.00/55.00 **st.**　　LT

⋔ **Mentone** without rest., 54-55 Cartwright Gdns., WC1H 9EL, ℰ 387 3927, Fax 388 4671, ※ – TV. 🖾 VISA ※ LT a
closed 21 to 26 December – **27 rm** ☲ 30.00/52.00 st.

⋔ **Russell House** without rest., 11 Bernard St., WC1N 1LN, ℰ 837 7686 – TV. ※ LU e
10 rm ☲ 45.00 t.

XX **Jamdani**, 34 Charlotte St., W1P 1HJ, ℰ 636 1178, Indian rest. – ⇔ ▤. 🖾 AE ⑩ VISA KU e
closed Sunday and 25-26 December – **M** 10.50/25.00 t. and a la carte.

XX **Neal Street**, 26 Neal St., WC2 9PH, ℰ 836 8368 – ▤. 🖾 AE ⑩ VISA
closed Saturday, Sunday, Christmas-New Year and Bank Holidays – **M** a la carte 30.00/
36.00 t. 🕯 7.50. p. 33 DV s

XX Mon Plaisir, 21 Monmouth St., WC2H 9DD, ℰ 836 7243, French rest. p. 33 DV a

XX Poons of Russell Square, 50 Woburn Pl., WC1H 0JE, ℰ 580 1188, Chinese rest. –
▤ LU x

XX **Kanishka**, 161 Whitfield St., W1P 5RY, ℰ 388 0860, Indian rest. – ▤. 🖾 ⑩ VISA
closed Saturday and Bank Holiday lunch and Sunday – **M** 6.95/12.00 t. and a la
carte. KTU z

X **Smith's**, 33 Shelton St., WC2H 9PU, ℰ 379 0310, Fax 836 8395 – 🖾 AE ⑩ VISA
closed Sunday and Bank Holidays – **M** 10.50 st. (dinner) and a la carte 19.25/23.00 st.
🕯 4.50. p. 33 DVX u

X **Auntie's**, 126 Cleveland St., W1P 5DN, ℰ 387 1548, English rest. – 🖾 AE ⑩ VISA
closed Saturday lunch and Sunday – **M** approx. 18.40 t. 🕯 5.20. JU s

X **Il Castelletto**, 17 Bury Pl., WC1A 21B, ℰ 405 2232, Italian rest. – ▤. 🖾 AE ⑩ VISA
closed Saturday lunch, Sunday and Bank Holidays – **M** 12.50 t. (lunch) and a la carte 16.40/
21.70 t. 🕯 4.65. LU r

Camden Town – ✉ NW1 – ✿ 071.

X **La Bougie**, 7 Murray St., NW1 9RE, ℰ 485 6400, Bistro KS a
closed Saturday lunch, Monday, last 2 weeks August, 2 weeks Christmas and Bank Holiday
Sundays – **M** a la carte 12.75/14.50 t. 🕯 3.75.

Euston – ✉ WC1 – ✿ 071.

🏨 **Scandic Crown**, 17/18 Upper Woburn Pl., WC1 0HT, ℰ 383 4105, Fax 412 0047, ⇔s – 🛗
⇔ rm ▤ TV ☎ க் – 🔬 120. 🖾 AE ⑩ VISA KT e
M 10.75/14.50 st. – **149 rm** 100.00/137.50 st., **1 suite** 219.00 st.

Finchley Road – ✉ NW3/NW6 – ✿ 071.

🏨 **Charles Bernard**, 5-7 Frognal, NW3 6AL, ℰ 794 0101, Telex 23560, Fax 794 0100 – 🛗 TV
☎ ⍉. 🖾 AE ⑩ VISA ※ ES s
M (bar lunch)/dinner a la carte 10.00/16.75 st. 🕯 4.00 – **57 rm** ☲ 47.50/79.50 st. –
SB (weekends only) 67.50/115.00 st.

Hampstead – ✉ NW3 – ✿ 071 – ♞ Winnington Rd ℰ 455 0203.

🏨 **Forte Posthouse**, 215 Haverstock Hill, NW3 4RB, ℰ 794 8121, Fax 435 5586 – 🛗 ⇔ rm
TV ☎ ⍉ – 🔬 30. 🖾 ⍉ ES r
M a la carte 9.55/20.90 st. 🕯 3.95 – ☲ 5.95 – **138 rm** 49.00 st.

🏨 **Clive** (Hilton), Primrose Hill Rd, NW3 3NA, ℰ 586 2233, Telex 22759, Fax 586 1659 – 🛗 TV
☎ ⍉ – 🔬 300. 🖾 AE ⑩ VISA ※ HS a
M (closed Saturday lunch) 9.95/12.95 st. and a la carte 🕯 5.10 – **93 rm** 45.00/71.00 s.,
3 suites 81.00 s. – SB (weekends only) 72.00/106.00 st.

🏨 **Swiss Cottage**, 4 Adamson Rd, NW3 3HP, ℰ 722 2281, Telex 297232, Fax 483 4588,
« Antique furniture collection » – 🛗 TV ☎ ⍉ – 🔬 60. 🖾 AE ⑩ VISA ※ GS n
M 14.95 t. and a la carte 🕯 4.75 – **61 rm** ☲ 50.00/140.00 t., **3 suites** 118.00/140.00 t.

🏨 **Langorf** without rest., 20 Frognal, NW3 6AG, ℰ 794 4483, Fax 435 9055 – 🛗 TV ☎. 🖾 AE
⑩ VISA – ☲ 5.50 – **31 rm** 61.00/83.00 st. ES c

XXX Benihana, 100 Avenue Rd, NW3 3HF, ℰ 586 9508, Fax 586 6740, Japanese Teppan-Yaki
rest. – ▤ GS o

XX **Carapace**, 118 Heath St., NW3 1DR, ℰ 435 8000 – 🖾 AE ⑩ VISA ES e
closed 26 December and 1 January – **M** (dinner only and Sunday lunch)/dinner 25.00 t.
and a la carte 🕯 4.00.

XX **Zen W3**, 83-84 Hampstead High St., NW3 1RE, ℰ 794 7863, Chinese rest. – 🖾 AE ⑩ VISA
closed 3 days at Christmas – **M** a la carte 21.10/31.00 t. 🕯 4.50. ES a

XX **Soong**, 459 South End Rd, NW3 2QB, ℰ 794 2461, Chinese (Szechuan) rest. – ▤. 🖾 AE
⑩ VISA – **M** 10.00/15.00 st. and a la carte. ES i

X **Chateaubriand**, 48 Belsize Lane, NW3 5AR, ℰ 435 4882 – 🖾 AE ⑩ VISA ES n
closed Sunday and 24 to 26 December – **M** (dinner only) 12.75 t. and a la carte 🕯 3.75.

Holborn – ✉ WC2 – ✿ 071.

🏨 **Drury Lane Moat House** (Q.M.H.), 10 Drury Lane, High Holborn, WC2B 5RE,
ℰ 836 6666, Telex 8811395, Fax 831 1548 – 🛗 ⇔ rm ▤ TV ☎ – 🔬 9.50 – **151 rm** 123.00/173.00 st., **2 suites** 300.00 st. –
M 13.25 t. and a la carte 🕯 9.00 – ☲ 9.50 – **151 rm** 123.00/173.00 st., **2 suites** 300.00 st. –
SB (weekends only) 140.00 st. p. 33 DV c

✗ **Imari**, 71 Red Lion St., WC1R 4NA, ☎ 405 0486, Fax 405 0473, Japanese rest. – 🗐, 🖾 [
① ☑️𝑆𝐴
MU
closed Saturday lunch, Sunday and Bank Holidays – **M** 19.00/22.00 **st.** and a la carte 🛔 4.0

Kentish Town – ⊠ NW5 - 🕾 071.

✗✗ **Bengal Lancer**, 253 Kentish Town Rd, NW5 2JT, ☎ 485 6688, Fax 482 4523, Indian res
– 🗐, 🖾 ⒶⒺ ① ☑️𝑆𝐴
JS
closed Saturday lunch and 25-26 December – **M** a la carte 10.50/18.00 **t.**

Regent's Park – ⊠ NW1 - 🕾 071.

🏨 **White House** (Rank), Albany St., NW1 3UP, ☎ 387 1200, Telex 24111, Fax 388 0091, 𝟏ₐ
⒤ ⥥ rm 🗐 ⒯⒱ ☎ ⅆ – 🕍 100. 🖾 ⒶⒺ ① ☑️𝑆𝐴. ⅏
JT
M 22.50 **st.** and a la carte 🛔 6.50 – ⥅ 10.75 – **561 rm** 118.00/153.00 **st.**, **15 suites** 198.00
355.00 **st.** – SB (weekends only) 84.00/92.00 **st.**

✗✗ **Odette's**, 130 Regent's Park Rd, NW1 8XL, ☎ 586 5486 – 🖾 ⒶⒺ ① ☑️𝑆𝐴
HS
closed Saturday lunch, Sunday, last 2 weeks August, 1 week Christmas and Bank Holiday
M a la carte 23.40/28.00 **t.** 🛔 5.95.

✗✗ **China Jazz**, 29-31 Parkway, NW1 7PN, ☎ 482 3940, Chinese rest.
JS

✗ **Koto**, 75 Parkway, NW1 7PP, ☎ 482 2036, Japanese rest.
JS

Swiss Cottage – ⊠ NW3 - 🕾 071.

🏨 **Holiday Inn**, 128 King Henry's Rd, NW3 3ST, ☎ 722 7711, Telex 267396, Fax 586 582
𝟏ₐ, ⥼, ⃞ – ⒤ ⥥ rm 🗐 ⒯⒱ ☎ & ⅆ – 🕍 400. 🖾 ⒶⒺ ① ☑️𝑆𝐴
GS
M 18.00 **t.** (lunch) and a la carte 17.75/27.95 **t.** 🛔 6.50 – ⥅ 11.25 – **295 rm** 135.00/157.50 **s**
8 suites 169.00/518.00 **st.**

✗✗ **Peter's**, 65 Fairfax Rd, NW6 4EE, ☎ 624 5804
FS

✗ **Thai Pepper**, 115 Finchley Rd, NW3 6HY, ☎ 722 0026, Thai rest. – 🗐, 🖾 ⒶⒺ ⓔ
☑️𝑆𝐴
GS
closed Saturday lunch, Sunday and Bank Holidays – **M** 17.00/20.00 **t.** and a la carte 🛔 4.45

CITY OF LONDON – 🕾 071 Except where otherwise stated see p. 23.

✗✗✗ 🕸 **Tatsuso**, 32 Broadgate Circle, EC2M 2QS, ☎ 638 5863, Fax 638 5864, Japanese rest.
🗐 🖾 ⒶⒺ ① ☑️𝑆𝐴
PU
closed Saturday, Sunday, 24 December-3 January and Bank Holidays – **M** (bookin
essential) 60.00/65.00 **t.** and a la carte 29.10/49.10 **t.**
Spec. Assorted marinated seaweed, Shabu-Shabu, Green tea ice cream.

✗✗ **Candlewick Room**, 45 Old Broad St., EC2N 1HT, ☎ 628 7929, French rest. – 🖾 ⒶⒺ ⓔ
☑️𝑆𝐴
PU
closed Saturday, Sunday and Bank Holidays – **M** (lunch only) 24.95 **t.** and a la carte 🛔 5.95

✗✗ **Le Poulbot** (basement), 45 Cheapside, EC2V 6AR, ☎ 236 4379, French rest. – 🗐. 🖾 [
① ☑️𝑆𝐴
OV
closed Saturday, Sunday and Bank Holidays – **M** (lunch only) 31.50 **st.**

✗✗ **Corney and Barrow**, 109 Old Broad St., EC2N 1AP, ☎ 638 9308 – 🗐. 🖾 🖾
☑️𝑆𝐴
PU
closed Saturday, Sunday and Bank Holidays – **M** (lunch only) 24.95 **t.** and a la carte 🛔 6.3

✗✗ **Corney and Barrow**, 118 Moorgate, EC2M 6UR, ☎ 628 2898 – 🗐
PU

✗✗ **Corney and Barrow**, 44 Cannon St., EC4N 6JJ, ☎ 248 1700 – 🗐. 🖾 ⒶⒺ ① ☑️𝑆𝐴 OV
closed Saturday, Sunday and Bank Holidays – **M** (lunch only) 19.50 **t.** and a la carte 🛔 7.9

✗✗ **Le Sous Sol**, 32 Old Bailey, EC4M 7HS, ☎ 236 7931, French rest. – 🖾 ⒶⒺ ☑️𝑆𝐴
closed Saturday, Sunday and Bank Holidays – **M** (lunch only) 24.50 **t.** 🛔 5.95. NV

✗✗ **Shares**, Beehive Passage, off Lime St., EC3M 7AA, ☎ 623 1843 – 🗐
PV

✗✗ **Miyama**, 17 Godliman St., EC4V 5BD, ☎ 489 1937, Japanese rest. – 🗐. 🖾 ⒶⒺ ① ☑️𝑆𝐴
closed Saturday, Sunday and Bank Holidays – **M** 16.00/38.00 **t.** and a la carte 🛔 5.00. OV

✗ **Bubb's**, 329 Central Market, Farringdon St., EC1A 9NB, ☎ 236 2435, French rest.
closed Saturday, Sunday, 2 weeks August, 1 week Christmas and Bank Holidays – ■
(booking essential) (lunch only) a la carte approx. 25.40 **st.** 🛔 4.85. NU

✗ **Whittington's**, 21 College Hill, EC4R 2RP, ☎ 248 5855 – 🗐. 🖾 ⒶⒺ ① ☑️𝑆𝐴 OV
closed Saturday, Sunday and Bank Holidays – **M** (lunch only) a la carte 20.20/24.35 🛦
🛔 4.50.

CROYDON pp. 10 and 11.

🖾 Addington Palace, Gravel Hill, Addington ☎ 654 3061.

Addington – ⊠ Surrey - 🕾 081.

🖾, 🖾, 🖾 Addington Court, Featherbed Lane ☎ 657 0281 – 🖾 The Addington, Shirl
Church Rd ☎ 777 1055.

✗✗ **Willow**, 88 Selsdon Park Rd, CR2 8JT, ☎ 657 4656, Chinese (Peking, Szechuan) rest
■ ⅆ. 🖾 ⒶⒺ ① ☑️𝑆𝐴
GZ
closed 25 to 28 December – **M** a la carte 16.50/23.50 **t.** 🛔 4.50.

Croydon – ⊠ Surrey – ☎ 081.

Coulsdon Court Municipal ✆ 660 0468 – Shirley Park, Addiscombe Rd ✆ 654 1143.

🛈 Katherine St. ✆ 760 5630, Fax 760 5634.

Croydon Park, 7 Altyre Rd, CR9 5AA, ✆ 680 9200, Telex 8956268, Fax 760 0426, *ƒ₆*, ≘s, ⊠, squash – ⧉ ⇔ rm 🔟 ☎ & ℗ – ⚘ 300. ◪ Æ � ⱽⁱⁿⁱ
FZ u
M 13.95/14.95 **st.** and a la carte – � 8.50 – **212 rm** 97.00/113.00 **st.** **2 suites** 225.00 **st.**

Forte Posthouse, Purley Way, CR9 4LT, ✆ 688 5185, Fax 681 6438, *⩷* – ⇔ rm 🔟 ☎ ℗
– ⚘ 170. ◪ Æ ⊙ ⱽⁱⁿⁱ
FZ o
M 10.95/13.95 **st.** and a la carte ⸔ 3.95 – ⊔ 5.95 – **85 rm** 49.50 **st.** – SB (except Christmas) (weekends only) 78.00 **st.**

Travel Inn, Coombe Rd, CR0 5RB, on A 212 ✆ 686 2030, Fax 686 6435 – ⇔ rm 🔟 & ℗.
◪ ◪ ⱽⁱⁿⁱ. ⩷
GZ s
M (Beefeater grill) a la carte approx. 13.50 **t.** – ⊔ 4.50 – **39 rm** 31.00 **t.**

Briarley, 8-10 Outram Rd, CR0 6XE, ✆ 654 1000, Fax 656 6084, *⩷* – 🔟 ☎ ℗. ◪ Æ ⊙
ⱽⁱⁿⁱ
M *(closed Sunday dinner and Bank Holidays)* (dinner only and Sunday lunch)/dinner 9.80 **t.**
and a la carte ⸔ 5.00 – **38 rm** ⊔ 54.50/64.50 **t.** – SB (weekends only) 69.10/98.60 **st.**

XX **Thirty Four Surrey Street**, 34 Surrey St., CR0 1RJ, ✆ 686 0586, Californian fish rest.,
Live jazz Friday and Saturday evenings – ◪ ⱽⁱⁿⁱ
FZ c
closed Saturday lunch and Sunday dinner – **M** a la carte 15.50/21.40 **t.** ⸔ 3.50.

X **Oh Boy**, 18 South End, CR0 1DN, ✆ 760 0278, Thai rest.
FZ a

X **Mario**, 299 High St., CR0 1QL, ✆ 686 5624, Italian rest. – **M** 10.20 **t.** (lunch) and a la
FZ v
carte 14.30/22.80 **t.**

Sanderstead – ⊠ Surrey – ☎ 081.

Selsdon Park Hotel, Addington Rd ✆ 657 8811.

Selsdon Park (Best Western), Addington Rd, CR2 8YA, ✆ 657 8811, Telex 945003,
Fax 651 6171, ≤, *ƒ₆*, ≘s, ⊒ heated, ⊠, , *⩷*, park, ⁒, squash – ⧉ ⇔ rm ☎ ℗ –
⚘ 150. ◪ Æ ⊙ ⱽⁱⁿⁱ
GZ n
M 20.00/29.00 **st.** and a la carte ⸔ 7.50 – ⊔ 8.50 – **163 rm** 103.00/158.00 **st.**, **7 suites**
235.00/280.00 **st.** – SB (weekends only) 142.00/174.00 **st.**

South Croydon – ⊠ Surrey – ☎ 081.

X **Kelong**, 1b Selsdon Rd, CR2 6PU, ✆ 688 0726, Malaysian, Singaporean rest. – ◪ Æ ⊙
ⱽⁱⁿⁱ
FZ v
closed Sunday and Bank Holidays – **M** 14.50/35.00 **t.** and a la carte.

EALING pp. 4 and 5.

Ealing – ⊠ W5 – ☎ 081.

Perivale Lane, Greenford ✆ 997 2595 – Horsenden Hill, Woodland Rise ✆ 902 4555.

Carnarvon, Ealing Common, W5 3HN, ✆ 992 5399, Telex 935114, Fax 992 7082 – ⧉
⇔ rm 🔟 ☎ ℗ – ⚘ 170. ◪ Æ ⊙ ⱽⁱⁿⁱ. ⩷
CV v
M 15.00/17.00 **st.** and a la carte ⸔ 5.50 – ⊔ 8.50 – **145 rm** 87.00/108.00 **st.** – SB (weekends
only) 64.00/70.00 **st.**

XX **Maxim**, 153-155 Northfield Av., W13 9QT, ✆ 567 1719, Chinese (Peking) rest. – ▦ ◪ BV a

XX **Laguna Tandoori**, 1-4 Culmington Par., Uxbridge Rd, W13 9BD, ✆ 579 9992, Indian
rest. – ▦, ◪ Æ ⊙ ⱽⁱⁿⁱ
BV i
closed 25 December – **M** 6.50/12.50 **st.** and a la carte ⸔ 3.15.

XX **Salotto**, Ealing Broadway Centre, 11 High St., W5 5DD, ✆ 840 7669, Italian rest. – ▦. ◪
Æ ⊙ ⱽⁱⁿⁱ
BV e
closed Saturday lunch, Sunday and Bank Holidays – **M** a la carte 16.30/23.50 **t.** ⸔ 4.50.

X **Noughts 'n' Crosses**, 77 The Grove, W5 5LL, ✆ 840 7568 – ◪ Æ ⱽⁱⁿⁱ
BV u
*closed Saturday lunch, Sunday dinner, Monday, Tuesday, August and 26 December-
4 January* – **M** (dinner only and Sunday lunch)/dinner 18.30 **t.**

X **Paolo's**, 7 Hanger Green, W5 3EL, ✆ 997 8560, Italian rest. – ◪ Æ ⊙ ⱽⁱⁿⁱ
CV r
closed Saturday lunch, Sunday and Bank Holidays except Christmas Day lunch – **M** a la
carte 17.80/15.20 **t.** ⸔ 3.60.

Hanwell – ⊠ W7 – ☎ 081.

Brent Valley, Church Rd, ✆ 567 1287.

X **New Happiness Garden**, 22 Boston Par., Boston Rd, W7 2DG, ✆ 567 9314, Chinese
rest. – ◪ Æ ⊙ ⱽⁱⁿⁱ
BV c
closed Sunday lunch, 25 December and 1 January – **M** 14.00/22.00 **t.** and a la carte ⸔ 4.00.

Southall – ⊠ Middx – ☎ 081.

West Middlesex, Greenford Rd ✆ 574 3450.

X **Brilliant**, 72-74 Western Rd, UB2 5DZ, ✆ 574 1928, Indian rest. – ▦. ◪ Æ ⊙ ⱽⁱⁿⁱ BV o
closed lunch Saturday and Sunday, Monday and August – **M** 12.50/15.00 **st.** and a la carte.

ENFIELD pp. 6 and 7.

🔓 Picketts Lock Sports Centre, Edmonton ♪ 803 3611.

Cockfosters – ⊠ Herts. – 🕾 081.
ET

XX Tandoori Nights, 27 Station Par., Cockfosters Rd, EN4 0DW, ♪ 441 2131, Indian rest. –

Enfield – ⊠ Middx – 🕾 081.

🔓 Whitewebbs, Beggars Hollow ♪ 363 2951, N : 1 m – 🔓 Crews Hill, Cattlegate Rd 363 0787, N : 2½ m. – 🔓 Old Park Road South ♪ 363 0313, NE : 1 m.

🏨 **Royal Chase,** 162 The Ridgeway, EN2 8AR, ♪ 366 6500, Telex 266628, Fax 367 7191, ET
🕸 – 📺 🕾 🅿 – 🔬 300. 🖪 🆎 ① 𝐕𝐈𝐒𝐀. 🕸
M *(closed Saturday lunch and Sunday dinner)* 15.95 **st.** (dinner) and a la carte 12.6
16.25 **st.** – **92 rm** ⊑ 45.00/94.00 **st.**

XXX **Norfolk,** 80 London Rd, EN2 6HU, ♪ 363 0979 – ▤. 🖪 🆎 ① 𝐕𝐈𝐒𝐀 FT
closed Saturday lunch, Monday dinner, Sunday and first 3 weeks August – **M** a carte 15.90/22.40 **t.** ᛳ 4.30.

Hadley Wood – ⊠ Herts – 🕾 081.

🔓 Beech Hill, Hadley Wood ♪ 449 4486.

🏨 **West Lodge Park** ⑤, off Cockfosters Rd, ⊠ Barnet, EN4 0PY, ♪ 440 831
Fax 449 3698, ≤, 🕸, park – 📲 📺 🕾 🕭 🅿 – 🔬 70. 🖪 🆎 𝐕𝐈𝐒𝐀. 🕸 ET
M 14.85 **t.** and a la carte ᛳ 5.25 – ⊑ 8.50 – **50 rm** 72.50/139.50 **st.** – SB (weekends on (except Christmas-New Year) 110.00 **st.**

GREENWICH pp. 10 and 11.

Blackheath – ⊠ SE3 – 🕾 081.

🏨 **Bardon Lodge,** 15-17 Stratheden Rd, SE3 7TH, ♪ 853 4051, Fax 858 7387, 🕸 – 📺 🕾 (HV
🖪 🆎 𝐕𝐈𝐒𝐀. 🕸
M *(closed Sunday dinner)* (bar lunch)/dinner 18.30 **t.** ᛳ 3.95 – **37 rm** ⊑ 49.00/82.00 **st.**

🏨 **Vanbrugh,** 21-23 St. John's Park, SE3 7JU, ♪ 853 5505 (reservations : 853 405
Fax 858 7387, 🕸 – 📲 📺 🕾 🅿. 🖪 🆎 𝐕𝐈𝐒𝐀. 🕸 HV
M (see **Bardon Lodge Hotel** above) – **30 rm** ⊑ 64.00/84.00 **st.**

Eltham – ⊠ SE9 – 🕾 081.

🔓 Royal Blackheath, Court Rd ♪ 850 1795.

↑ **Meadow Croft Lodge** without rest., 96-98 Southwood Rd, New Eltham, SE9 3C
♪ 859 1488, 🕸 – 📺 🅿. 𝐕𝐈𝐒𝐀. 🕸 JX
17 rm ⊑ 21.00/42.00 **st.**

↑ **Yardley Court** without rest., 18 Court Yard, SE9 5PZ, ♪ 850 1850, 🕸 – 📺 🅿. 🖪 𝐕𝐈𝐒𝐀
9 rm ⊑ 32.00/52.00 **st.** HX

Greenwich – ⊠ SE10 – 🕾 081.

🅿 46 Greenwich Church St. ♪ 858 6376.

XX **Treasure of China,** 10 Nelson Rd, SE10 9JB, ♪ 858 9884, Chinese (Peking, Szechua rest. – ▤. 🖪 🆎 ① 𝐕𝐈𝐒𝐀 GV
M 15.00/25.00 **t.** and a la carte ᛳ 3.50.

X **Spread Eagle,** 1-2 Stockwell St., SE10 9JL, ♪ 853 2333 – 🖪 🆎 ① 𝐕𝐈𝐒𝐀 GV
closed 25 to 30 December and Bank Holidays – **M** *(closed Saturday lunch)* (lunch arrangement Monday to Saturday) dinner 25.00 **t.** and a la carte 16.00/23.00 **t.** ᛳ 3.50.

X **Taste of India,** 57 Greenwich Church St., SE10 9BL, ♪ 858 2668, Indian rest. – 🖪 🆎
𝐕𝐈𝐒𝐀 – **M** 9.50/14.00 **t.** and a la carte. GV

HACKNEY p. 23.

Liverpool Street – ⊠ EC2 – 🕾 071.

XX **Equities,** 1 Finsbury Av., EC2M 2PA, ♪ 247 1051 – ▤. 🖪 🆎 ① 𝐕𝐈𝐒𝐀 PU
closed Saturday, Sunday and Bank Holidays – **M** (lunch only) 17.50/27.00 **t.** ᛳ 4.50.

Dalston – ⊠ N 1 – 🕾 071.

X **Soulard,** 113 Mortimer Rd, N1 4JY, ♪ 254 1314, French rest. – 🖪 🆎 𝐕𝐈𝐒𝐀 PS
closed Saturday lunch, Sunday, Monday, last 2 weeks August and 1 week Christmas –
14.50 **t.** (lunch) and a la carte 11.50/16.00 **t.** ᛳ 6.50.

HAMMERSMITH and FULHAM Except where otherwise stated see pp. 24-25.

Fulham – ⊠ SW6 – 🕾 071.
p. 12 BQ

🏨 **La Reserve,** 422-428 Fulham Rd, SW6 1DU, ♪ 385 8561, Fax 385 7662, « Contempor
decor » – 📲 🕸 rm 📺 🕾. 🖪 🆎 ① 𝐕𝐈𝐒𝐀. 🕸 FZ
M 25.00/30.00 **t.** and a la carte – ⊑ 3.00 – **40 rm** 75.00/110.00 **st.**

XX Hiders, 755 Fulham Rd, SW6, ☎ 736 2331   p. 12 BQ a

XX **Blue Elephant**, 4-6 Fulham Broadway, SW6 1AA, ☎ 385 6595, Fax 386 7665, Thai rest.
■. ☒ ℂ *VISA*   EZ z
closed Saturday lunch and 24 to 27 December – **M** (booking essential) 25.00/28.00 **t.**
and a la carte ╽ 5.35.

XX Hot Gossip, 593-599 Fulham Rd, SW6 5UA, ☎ 386 0506, Fax 386 0467, Japanese Teppa-
nyaki and Chinese rests. – ■.   EZ a

XX **Chin's**, 311-313 New Kings Rd, SW6 4RF, ☎ 736 8833, Chinese rest. – ■. ☒ ℂ ⓪ *VISA*
M 19.00/29.00 **st.** and a la carte ╽ 4.60.   p. 12 BQ n

XX **Mao Tai**, 58 New Kings Rd., Parsons Green, SW6 4UG, ☎ 731 2520, Chinese (Szechuan)
rest. – ■. ☒ ℂ ⓪ *VISA*   p. 12 BQ e
M 17.50 **t.** and a la carte ╽ 7.50.

XX **Nayab**, 309 New Kings Rd, SW6 4RF, ☎ 731 6993, Indian rest. – ☒ ℂ ⓪ *VISA*
closed 25 to 26 December and 1 January – **M** a la carte 11.20/16.35 **t.**   p. 12 BQ i

X **Le Midi**, 488 Fulham Rd, SW6, ☎ 386 0657 – ☒ ℂ *VISA*   EZ a
closed lunch Saturday and Bank Holidays – **M** 10.95 **t.** (lunch) and a la carte 14.40/20.45 **t.**
╽ 4.00.

Hammersmith – ✉ W6/W12/W14 – ☎ 081.

XX **Tandoori Nights**, 319-321 King St., W6 9NH, ☎ 741 4328, Indian rest. – ■. ☒ ℂ ⓪ *VISA*
closed 25 and 26 December – **M** 8.95 **st.** and a la carte approx. 15.00 **st.** ╽ 4.25. p. 9 CV u

X **Garden**, 210 King St., W6 0RA, ☎ 748 5058, Korean rest.   p. 9 CV a
M 7.00/24.00 **t.** and a la carte.

Shepherd's Bush – ✉ W12/W14 – ☎ 071.

X **Chinon**, 25 Richmond Way, W14 0AS, ☎ 602 5968 – ■. ☒ ℂ *VISA*   p. 9 DV s
closed Sunday, 2 weeks August-September and Bank Holidays – **M** 18.50 **t.** and a la
carte 35.00/39.50 **t.**

West Kensington – ✉ SW6/W14 – ☎ 071.

🏨 **Ramada Inn West London**, 44 Lillie Rd, SW6 1UQ, ☎ 385 1255, Telex 917728,
Fax 381 4450 – 🛗 ⇖ rm ■ rest 📺 ☎ 🅿 – 🔒 1 750. ☒ ℂ ⓪ ℇ *VISA*. ⚜
M a la carte 13.70/24.25 **st.** – ⥥ 8.70 **497 rm** 80.00/90.00 **st.**, **4 suites** 125.00 **st.** –
SB (weekends only) 84.00/120.00 **st.**   p.24 EZ e

🏠 **Aston Court** without rest., 25-27 Matheson Rd, W14 8SN, ☎ 602 9954, Telex 919208,
Fax 371 1338 – 🛗 📺 ☎. ☒ ℂ *VISA*. ⚜   p. 24 EZ i
29 rm ⥥ 59.50/82.50 **st.**

HARINGEY pp. 6 and 7.

Hornsey – ✉ N8 – ☎ 081.

X **Jashan**, 19a Turnpike Lane, N8 0EP, ☎ 340 9880, Indian rest. – ■. ☒ ℂ ⓪ *VISA*   EU z
M a la carte approx. 15.00 **t.** ╽ 5.95.

X **Le Bistro**, 36 High St., N8 7NX, ☎ 340 2116 – ☒ *VISA*   EU u
closed Sunday, last 3 weeks August and Bank Holidays – **M** a la carte 12.25/14.95 **t.**
and a la carte ╽ 2.75.

HARROW pp. 4 and 5.

Central Harrow – ✉ Middx – ☎ 081.
🖼 Civic Centre, Station Rd ☎ 424 1103/424 1102, Fax 427 8496.

🏨 **Cumberland**, 1 St. John's Rd, HA1 2EF, ☎ 863 4111, Telex 917201, Fax 861 5668 –
⇖ rm 📺 ☎ 🅿. ☒ ℂ ⓪ *VISA*. ⚜   BU x
M 6.95/11.95 **st.** and a la carte ╽ 4.50 – **80 rm** ⥥ 62.00/75.00 **st.**

X **Trattoria Sorrentina**, 6 Manor Parade, Sheepcote Rd, HA1 2JA, ☎ 427 9411, Italian
rest. – ☒ ⓪ *VISA*   BU x
closed Saturday lunch, Sunday and Bank Holidays – **M** a la carte 20.45/27.75 **t.** ╽ 4.50.

Hatch End – ✉ Middx – ☎ 081 – 🏌 Grims Dyke, Oxhey Lane ☎ 428 4093.

X **Swan**, 322-326 Uxbridge Rd, HA5 4RH, ☎ 428 8821, Chinese (Peking) rest. – ■   BT n
M (buffet lunch Sunday) 16.00 **t.** (dinner) and a la carte 27.20/50.60 **t.**

Kenton – ✉ Middx. – ☎ 081.

🏠 **Travel Inn**, Kenton Rd, HA3 8AT, ☎ 907 1671, Fax 909 1604 – ⇖ rm 📺 ♿ 🅿. ☒ ℂ ⓪
VISA. ⚜   BU e
closed 24 to 26 December – **M** (Beefeater grill) a la carte approx. 13.50 **t.** – ⥥ 4.50 – **44 rm**
31.00 **t.**

North Harrow – ✉ Middx. – ☎ 081.

X Thai Castle, 28 The Broadwalk, Pinner Rd, HA2 6ED, ☎ 427 4732, Thai rest.   BU c

Rayner's Lane – ✉ Middx. – ☎ 081.

XX Piins 453 Alexandra Av., HA2 9SE, ℘ 868 9085, Fax 429 1628, Chinese (Szechua Peking rest.) – ▤ BU

Stanmore – ✉ Middx – ☎ 081.

Gordon Av. ℘ 954 4661.

X **Mr Tang's Mandarin** 28 The Broadway, HA7 4DW, ℘ 954 0339, Chinese (Peking) re – ▤. AE VISA BT
M a la carte 15.00/20.00 **t.** 3.50.

HAVERING pp. 6 and 7.

Hornchurch by A 12 – JT – on A 127 – ✉ Essex – ☎ 040 23 (5 fig.) and 07 (6 fig.) Ingrebourne.

Hilton National, Southend Arterial Rd (A 127), RM11 3UJ, ℘ 46789, Telex 89731 Fax 41719 – rm TV ☎ & P – 200. AE VISA
M *(closed Saturday lunch)* 13.00/33.00 **t.** and a la carte 4.95 – ☕ 9.00 – **137 r** 86.00/140.00 **st.**

Romford by A 118 – JU – ✉ Essex – ☎ 0708.

18, 9 Havering, Risebridge Chase ℘ 41429.

Coach House without rest., 48 Main Rd, RM1 3DB, on A 118 ℘ 751901, Fax 730290, TV P.
32 rm ☕ 26.95/50.00 **s.**

HILLINGDON pp. 4 and 8.

18 Haste Hill, The Drive ℘ 092 74 (Northwood) 22877 – 18 Harefield Pl., The Drive ℘ 08 (Uxbridge) 31169, by B 467 – 9 18 Dorset Way ℘ 0895 (Uxbridge) 39810.

Eastcote – ✉ Middx – ☎ 081.

18 Ruislip, Ickenham Rd ℘ 0895 (Ruislip) 632004.

X **Sambuca,** 113 Field End Rd, HA5 1QG, ℘ 866 7500, Italian rest. – AE VISA AU
M (dinner only and Sunday lunch)/dinner 12.40/17.70 **t.** and a la carte 3.70.

Hayes – ✉ Middx. – ☎ 081.

Travel Inn, 362 Uxbridge Rd, UB4 0HF, ℘ 573 7479, Fax 569 1204 – rm TV & P. AE VISA. AV
M (Beefeater grill) a la carte approx. 13.50 **t.** 4.50 – ☕ 4.50 – **40 rm** 31.00 **t.**

Heathrow Airport – ✉ Middx – ☎ 081.

Underground Station Concourse, Heathrow Airport ℘ (071) 730 3488.

Edwardian International, 140 Bath Rd, UB3 5AW, ℘ 759 6311, Telex 23935, Fax 759 455 – rm ▤ TV ☎ P – 500. AE VISA. AX
M *(closed Saturday lunch)* 27.00/33.00 **st.** and a la carte 6.50 – **442 rm, 17 suites.**

Excelsior Heathrow (Forte), Bath Rd, West Drayton, UB7 0DU, ℘ 759 6611, Tel 24525, Fax 759 3421 – rm ▤ TV ☎ & P – 700. AE VISA.
M *(closed Saturday lunch)* 14.95/21.50 **st.** and a la carte 4.35 – ☕ 9.50 – **523 rm** 105.0 145.00 **st., 16 suites** 215.00 **st.** – SB (weekends only) 118.00 **st.** AX

Sheraton Skyline, Bath Rd, Hayes, UB3 5BP, ℘ 759 2535, Telex 934254, Fax 750 915 « Exotic indoor garden », – rm ▤ TV ☎ & P – 500. AE VISA
M 23.70/35.70 **t.** and a la carte 6.00 – ☕ 10.75 – **347 rm** 125.00/160.00 **s., 5 suit** 310.00/700.00 **st.** – SB (weekends only) 241.00/299.80 **st.** AX

Sterling, Terminal 4, TW6 3AF, ℘ 759 7755, Telex 925094, Fax 759 7579, – rm ▤ TV ☎ & P – 240 AX
393 rm, 4 suites.

Holiday Inn, Stockley Rd, West Drayton, UB7 9NA, ℘ 0895 (West Drayton) 44555 Telex 934518, Fax 445122, 9 – rm ▤ TV ☎ & P – 120. AE V
M 15.70/19.95 **t.** and a la carte 6.05 – ☕ 9.50 – **379 rm** 98.00/113.00 **st., 1 sui** 250.00/485.00 **st.** – SB (weekends only) 94.00/188.00 **st.** AV

Sheraton Heathrow, Colnbrook by-pass, West Drayton, UB7 0HJ, ℘ 759 2424, Tel 934331, Fax 759 2091, – rm ▤ TV ☎ P – 70. AE VISA. AVX
M 14.00 **st.** and a la carte 3.50 – ☕ 10.00 – **414 rm** 95.00/160.00 **st., 1 suite** 125.00 **st.**

Forte Crest, Sipson Rd, West Drayton, UB7 0JU, ℘ 759 2323, Telex 93428 Fax 897 8659, – rm ▤ TV ☎ P – 200. AE VISA AV
M 14.95 **st.** and a la carte 4.50 – ☕ 9.50 – **565 rm** 85.00/110.00 **st., 4 suites** 170.00 st SB (weekends only) 98.00 **st.**

Heathrow Penta, Bath Rd, Hounslow, TW6 2AQ, ℘ 897 6363, Telex 93466 Fax 897 1113, – ▤ TV ☎ P – 450. AE VISA. AX
M *(bar lunch Saturday and Sunday)* 15.00/16.00 **st.** and a la carte – ☕ 9.00 – **627** 95.00/142.50 **st., 9 suites** 185.00/425.00 **st.**

🏨 **Heathrow Park** (Mt. Charlotte Thistle), Bath Rd, Longford, West Drayton, UB7 0EQ, ℰ 759 2400, Telex 934093, Fax 759 5278 – 🛬 rm 🔲 📺 ☎ 🅿 – 🔬 600. 🔼 🆎 ⑩ 🆅🆂🅰
M (bar meals Saturday lunch and Sunday) (carving lunch Monday to Friday) /dinner 15.25 **st.** and a la carte ⓙ 5.70 – ☑ 8.25 – **306 rm** 85.00/145.00 **st.** off A 4 AX

🏨 **Forte Posthouse,** Bath Rd, Hayes, UB3 5AJ, ℰ 759 2552, Telex 21777, Fax 564 9265 – 📳
🛬 rm 🔲 📺 ☎ 🅿. 🔼 🆎 ⑩ 🆅🆂🅰 AX i
M (carving rest.) 10.50/17.00 **st.** ⓙ 3.95 – ☑ 7.95 – **180 rm** 65.00 **st.** – SB (weekends only) 78.00 **st.**

Ickenham – ✉ Middx. – ☎ 0895 Ruislip

✗ **Roberto's,** 15 Long Lane, UB10 8TB, ℰ 632519, Italian rest. – 🔼 🆎 🆅🆂🅰 AU i
closed Sunday and last 2 weeks August – **M** a la carte 15.00/24.50 **t.** ⓙ 4.50.

Yiewsley – ✉ Middx. – ☎ 081.

✗✗ **L'Esprit,** The Arena, Stockley Park, UB11 1AA, ℰ 573 7333, Fax 561 0550 – ■ 🅿. 🔼
⑩ 🆅🆂🅰 AV s
closed Saturday lunch, dinner Monday to Wednesday, Sunday, 24 December-1 January and Bank Holidays – **M** 16.25 **st.** (lunch) and a la carte 16.15/25.95 **st.** ⓙ 6.00.

HOUNSLOW pp. 8 and 9.

Wyke Green, Syon Lane, Isleworth ℰ (081) 560 8777, ½ m. from Gillettes Corner (A 4).

Chiswick – ✉ W4 – ☎ 081.

✗✗ **Chow Shing,** 1-3 Acton Lane, W4 5NE, ℰ 994 6829, Chinese (Szechuan), and Vietnamese rest. – ▤. 🔼 🆎 🆅🆂🅰 CV i
M 15.00/21.00 **st.** and a la carte ⓙ 3.00.

✗✗ **Antonio's,** 6-8 Elliott Rd, W4 1PE, ℰ 742 1485, Italian rest. – 🔼 🆎 🆅🆂🅰 CV o
closed 25-26 December and 1 January – **M** 10.00/20.00 **t.** and a la carte ⓙ 4.00.

✗✗ Grove Park, 313 Chiswick High Rd, W4 4HH, ℰ 995 3354, Chinese (Peking) rest. CV i

✗ **La Dordogne,** 5 Devonshire Rd, W4 2EU, ℰ 747 1836, Fax 994 9144, French rest. – 🔼 🆎
🆅🆂🅰 CV o
closed Saturday and Sunday lunch and Bank Holidays – **M** a la carte 17.20/25.20 **t.**

✗ **Annapurna,** 101 Chiswick High Rd, W4 2ED, ℰ 995 4431, Indian rest. CV n
M a la carte approx. 7.50 **t.** ⓙ 3.75.

Cranford – ✉ Middx. – ☎ 081.

🏨 Berkeley Arms (Jarvis), Bath Rd, TW5 9QE, ℰ 897 2121, Telex 935728, Fax 759 7154 – 📳
📺 ☎ 🅿 – 🔬 70 – **56 rm.** AX r

Heston Service Area – ✉ Middx. – ☎ 081.

🏨 **Granada Lodge** without rest., on M 4 (westbound carriageway), TW5 9NA, ℰ 574 5875, Fax 574 1891 – 📺 ♿ 🅿. 🔼 🆎 ⑩ 🆅🆂🅰 – **46 rm** 39.00/43.00 **st.** ABV e

Hounslow – ✉ Middx. – ☎ 081.

🏌 Airlinks, Southall Lane ℰ 561 1418 – 🏌 Hounslow Heath, Staines Rd ℰ 570 5271.

✗✗ **Hee's,** 476-478 Great West Rd (A 4), TW5 0TA, ℰ 577 3817, Chinese (Peking, Szechuan) rest. – ▤. 🔼 🆎 ⑩ 🆅🆂🅰 BX r
closed 25 to 28 December – **M** 12.00/19.50 **t.** and a la carte.

ISLINGTON Except where otherwise stated see pp. 20-23.

Canonbury – ✉ N1 – ☎ 071.

✗ **Anna's Place,** 90 Mildmay Park, N1 4PR, ℰ 249 9379, Swedish rest.
closed Sunday, Monday, 2 weeks Easter, August and 2 weeks Christmas – **M** (booking essential) a la carte 13.10/17.20 **t.** p. 6 FU a

Finsbury – ✉ WC1/EC1/EC2 – ☎ 071.

✗ **Le Mesurier,** 113 Old St., EC1V 9JR, ℰ 251 8117 – 🔼 🆎 ⑩ 🆅🆂🅰 OT e
closed Saturday, Sunday, 3 weeks August and 1 week Christmas – **M** (lunch only) (booking essential) a la carte 21.50/26.00 **t.** ⓙ 4.50.

✗ **Rouxl Britannia,** Triton Court, 14 Finsbury Sq., EC2A 1RP, ℰ 256 6997 – ▤. 🔼 🆎 ⑩
🆅🆂🅰 PU x
M Le Restaurant (closed Saturday and Sunday) (lunch only) 19.85 **st.** ⓙ 5.30 – **Le Café** (closed Saturday and Sunday) (lunch only) a la carte approx. 11.45 **st.** ⓙ 5.30.

✗ **Quality Chop House,** 94 Farringdon Rd, EC1R 3EA, ℰ 837 5093 MT n
closed Saturday lunch, and 10 days at Christmas – **M** a la carte 14.25/18.75 **t.**

✗ **Lakorn,** 197-199 Rosebery Av., EC1R 4TJ, ℰ 837 5048, Thai rest. – 🔼 🆎 🆅🆂🅰 NT e
closed Saturday lunch, Sunday and Bank Holidays – **M** a la carte approx. 12.00 **t.**

Islington – ⊠ N1 – ☎ 071.

✗ **Mon Plaisir du Nord,** The Mall, 359 Upper St., N1 0PD, ✆ 359 1932, Fax 704 29
French rest. – ▤. 🔼 AE ⓪ VISA
closed Saturday lunch, Sunday and Bank Holidays – **M** 13.70 t. (lunch) and a la carte 15.
21.05 t. ≬ 4.90. NS

✗ **Neshiko,** 265 Upper St., N1 2UQ, ✆ 359 9977, Japanese rest. – 🔼 AE ⓪ VISA NS
closed Sunday – **M** 10.00/55.00 t. and a la carte ≬ 9.95.

Upper Holloway – ⊠ N19 – ☎ 071.

✗ **Raj Vogue,** 34 Highgate Hill, N19 5NL, ✆ 272 9091, Indian rest. – 🔼 AE ⓪ VISA
closed 25 December – **M** 10.50/20.00 st. and a la carte ≬ 6.50. p.6 EU

KENSINGTON and CHELSEA (Royal Borough of).

Chelsea – ⊠ SW1/SW3/SW10 – ☎ 071 – Except where otherwise stated see pp.
and 31.

🏨 **Hyatt Carlton Tower,** 2 Cadogan Pl., SW1X 9PY, ✆ 235 5411, Telex 219
Fax 245 6570, ≤, ƒ₆, ≘ѕ, 灬, ఞ – ▯ ୰ rm ▤ ⊡ ☎ ⟿ Ɒ – 🔏 300. 🔼 AE ⓪ VISA ⋘
M Chelsea Room 25.50/32.00 **st.** and a la carte – **Rib Room** 22.50/32.00 **st.** and a la ca
≬ 7.50 – � 12.75 – **194 rm** 220.00 s., **30 suites** 320.00/2 000.00 s. FR

🏨 **Conrad Chelsea Harbour,** Chelsea Harbour, SW10 0XG, ✆ 823 3000, Telex 9192
Fax 351 6525, ≤, ƒ₆, ≘ѕ, ▣ – ▯ ୰ rm ▤ ⊡ ☎ ♿ Ɒ – 🔏 180. 🔼 AE ⓪ VISA ⋘
M 16.00 t. (lunch) and a la carte 19.50/26.00 t. –. **160 suites** 195.00/1 000.00 s. p. 9 EX

🏨 **Sheraton Park Tower,** 101 Knightsbridge, SW1X 7RN, ✆ 235 8050, Telex 9172
Fax 235 8231, ≤ – ▯ ୰ rm ▤ ⊡ ☎ ♿ Ɒ – 🔏 80. 🔼 AE ⓪ VISA ⋘
M 22.00/25.00 **st.** and a la carte ≬ 7.50 – ⊡ 14.50 – **267 rm** 195.00/280.00 s., **22 suit**
395.00/1 050.00 s. FQ

🏨 **Durley House,** 115 Sloane St., SW1X 9PJ, ✆ 235 5537, Telex 919235, Fax 259 69
« Tastefully furnished Georgian town house », ఞ – ▯ ⊡ ☎. 🔼 VISA ⋘ FS
M (room service only) a la carte 12.00/22.50 t. ≬ 6.00 – ⊡ 10.50 – **11 suites** 250.
300.00 t.

🏨 ۞ **Capital,** 22-24 Basil St., SW3 1AT, ✆ 589 5171, Telex 919042, Fax 225 0011 – ▯ ▤
☎. 🔼 AE ⓪ VISA ⋘ ER
M 20.00/25.00 **st.** and a la carte 36.00/40.50 **st.** – ⊡ 10.50 – **48 rm** 165.00/285.00 **st.**
Spec. Composed salad of french leaves with crab, peppers and caviar, Poêlé of rabbit truffle, leek and carrots, Parfa
Poire Williams with a warm pear Pithivier.

🏨 **Cadogan,** 75 Sloane St., SW1X 9SG, ✆ 235 7141, Telex 267893, Fax 245 0994 – ▯ ୰
⊡ ☎ – 🔏 40. 🔼 AE ⓪ VISA ⋘
closed until mid 1992 for refurbishment – **M** 24.00/29.00 **st.** and a la carte ≬ 6.50 – ⊡ 10
– **64 rm** 159.00/199.00 **st.**, **5 suites** 275.00/325.00 **st.**

🏨 **Draycott,** 24-26 Cadogan Gdns, SW3 2RP, ✆ 730 6466, Fax 730 0236 – ▯ ⊡ ☎. 🔼
⓪ VISA ⋘ FS
M (room service only) – ⊡ 9.25 – **24 rm** 75.00/250.00 t.

🏨 **Fenja** without rest., 69 Cadogan Gdns, SW3 2RB, ✆ 589 7333, Telex 9342
Fax 581 4958 – ▯ ⊡ ☎. 🔼 VISA ⋘ FS
⊡ 10.50 – **13 rm** 105.00/210.00 st.

🏨 **Chelsea,** 17-25 Sloane St., SW1X 9NU, ✆ 235 4377, Telex 919111, Fax 235 3705 –
୰ rm ▤ ⊡ ☎ – 🔏 120. 🔼 AE ⓪ VISA ⋘ FR
M *(closed Bank Holidays)* 15.00/25.00 **st.** and a la carte ≬ 5.00 – ⊡ 9.75 – **218 rm** 141.
172.00 st., **7 suites** 195.00/280.00 st.

🏨 **Basil Street,** 8 Basil St., SW3 1AH, ✆ 581 3311, Telex 28379, Fax 581 3693 – ▯ ⊡ ☎
🔏 55 FQ
91 rm, **1 suite.**

🏨 **Egerton House,** 17-19 Egerton Terr., SW3 2BX, ✆ 589 2412, Fax 584 6540 – ▯ ▤ ⊡
🔼 AE ⓪ VISA ⋘ DR
M (room service only) a la carte 15.00/38.00 **st.** – ⊡ 12.50 – **27 rm** 98.00/190.00 st., **1 su**
230.00 st.

🏨 **Beaufort,** 33 Beaufort Gdns, SW3 1PP, ✆ 584 5252, Telex 929200, Fax 589 2834, « E
glish floral watercolour collection » – ▯ ୰ rm ▤ ⊡ ☎. 🔼 AE ⓪ VISA ⋘ ER
closed 22 December-2 January – **M** (room service only) – **28 rm** ⊡ 150.00/250.00 s
SB (November-April) (weekends only) 80.00/110.00 st.

🏨 **Royal Court** (Q.M.H.), Sloane Sq., SW1W 8EG, ✆ 730 9191, Telex 296818, Fax 824 8
– ▯ ▤ rest ⊡ ☎ – 🔏 40. 🔼 AE ⓪ VISA ⋘ FST
M *(closed Saturday lunch and Sunday dinner)* 12.50 **st.** and a la carte ≬ 5.00 – ⊡ 9.2
102 rm 92.00/117.00 **st.** – SB (weekends only) 130.00 **st.**

🏨 **Eleven Cadogan Gardens,** 11 Cadogan Gardens, SW3 2RJ, ✆ 730 3426, Fax 730 52
– ▯ ☎. 🔼 AE ⓪ VISA ⋘
M (room service only) – ⊡ 8.50 – **56 rm** 89.00/200.00 st., **5 suites** 200.00/350.00 st.

L'Hotel without rest., 28 Basil St., SW3 1AT, ℰ 589 6286, Telex 919042, Fax 225 0011 – |‡| ⬜ ☎. ⬛ ⟪ℰ⟫ *VISA* — ER **i**
12 rm 110.00/145.00 **t.**

Parkes without rest., 41-43 Beaufort Gdns, SW3 1PW, ℰ 581 9944, Telex 922488, Fax 225 3447 – |‡| ⬜ ☎. ⬛ ⟪ℰ⟫ ⓞ *VISA*. ⬤ — ER **c**
17 rm ⬜ 103.00/138.00, **16 suites** 230.00.

Willett without rest., 32 Sloane Gdns, Sloane Sq., SW1W 8DJ, ℰ 824 8415, Telex 926678, Fax 824 8415 – ⬜ ☎. ⬛ ⟪ℰ⟫ ⓞ *VISA*. ⬤ — FT **s**
18 rm ⬜ 60.45/76.95 **s.**

Claverley without rest., 13-14 Beaufort Gdns, SW3 1PS, ℰ 589 8541, Fax 584 3410 – |‡| ⬤ ⬜ ☎. ⬛ ⟪ℰ⟫ *VISA*. ⬤ — ER **o**
32 rm ⬜ 50.00/150.00 **t.**

Executive without rest., 57 Pont St., SW1X 0BD, ℰ 581 2424, Telex 9413498, Fax 589 9456 – |‡| ⬜ ☎. ⬛ ⟪ℰ⟫ ⓞ *VISA*. ⬤ — ER **v**
29 rm ⬜ 54.95/79.95.

Wilbraham, 1-5 Wilbraham Pl., Sloane St., SW1X 9AE, ℰ 730 8296, Fax 730 6815 – |‡| ☎. ⬤ — FS **n**
M *(closed Saturday lunch, Sunday and Bank Holidays)* (restricted menu) a la carte 11.15/ 16.45 **t.** ⟨ 3.45 – ⬜ 5.50 – **53 rm** 40.00/86.00.

XX ⬤⬤ **La Tante Claire** (Koffmann), 68-69 Royal Hospital Rd, SW3 4HP, ℰ 352 6045, Fax 352 3257, French rest. – ⬛. ⬛ ⟪ℰ⟫ ⓞ *VISA* — EU **c**
closed Saturday, Sunday, Christmas-New Year and Bank Holidays – **M** 23.50 **st.** (lunch) and a la carte 49.00/60.50 **st.**
Spec. Coquilles St. Jacques rôties, sauce encre, Assiette canardière, Saumon confit à l'huile d'olive et pipérade.

XX **Waltons,** 121 Walton St., SW3 2HP, ℰ 584 0204 – ⬛. ⬛ ⟪ℰ⟫ ⓞ *VISA* — DS **a**
closed 25 and 26 December – **M** 14.75/21.00 **t.** and a la carte ⟨ 4.50.

XX **Dynasty II,** Chelsea Wharf, 15 Lots Rd, SW10 0QJ, ℰ 351 1020, ≼, Oriental cuisine, « Riverside setting » – ⬛ ⓟ. ⬛ ⟪ℰ⟫ ⓞ *VISA* — p. 25 GZ **n**
M 25.00/35.00 **t.** and a la carte 20.00/31.00 **t.** ⟨ 5.00.

XX **Turner's,** 87-89 Walton St., SW3 2HP, ℰ 584 6711, Fax 584 4441 – ⬛. ⬛ ⟪ℰ⟫ ⓞ *VISA* — ES **n**
closed Saturday lunch, 25 to 30 December and Bank Holidays – **M** 18.50/29.50 **st.** and a la carte ⟨ 8.00.

XX **Bibendum,** Michelin House, 81 Fulham Rd, SW3 6RD, ℰ 581 5817, Fax 823 7925 – ⬛. ⬛ *VISA* — DS **s**
closed 3 days at Christmas – **M** 26.00 **t.** (lunch) and a la carte 26.25/50.00 **t.** ⟨ 5.25.

XX Zen, Chelsea Cloisters, Sloane Av., SW3 3DW, ℰ 589 1781, Chinese rest. – ⬛ — ET **a**

XX **Chutney Mary,** 535 King's Rd, SW10 0SZ, ℰ 351 3113, Anglo-Indian rest. – ⬛. ⬛ ⟪ℰ⟫ ⓞ *VISA* — FZ **v**
M a la carte 20.20/29.25.

XX **Daphne's,** 110-112 Draycott Av., SW3 3AE, ℰ 589 4257 – ⬛. ⬛ ⟪ℰ⟫ ⓞ *VISA* — DS **e**
closed Saturday lunch, Sunday dinner and Bank Holidays – **M** 18.00/28.00 **t.** and a la carte ⟨ 4.50.

XX Salotto, 257-259 Fulham Rd, SW3 6HY, ℰ 351 1383, Italian rest. – ⬛ — p. 9 CU **i**

XX La Finezza, 62-64 Lower Sloane St., SW1N 8BP, ℰ 730 8639, Italian rest. – ⬛ — FT **v**

XX **English Garden,** 10 Lincoln St., SW3 2TS, ℰ 584 7272, English rest. – ⬛. ⬛ ⟪ℰ⟫ ⓞ *VISA* — ET **x**
closed 25 and 26 December – **M** 16.25 **t.** (lunch) and a la carte 19.25/25.95 **t.** ⟨ 4.50.

XX **Gavvers,** 61-63 Lower Sloane St., SW1W 8DH, ℰ 730 5983, French rest. – ⬛. ⬛ ⟪ℰ⟫ ⓞ *VISA* — FT **e**
closed Saturday lunch, Sunday and Bank Holidays – **M** 16.25/30.75 **st.** and a la carte ⟨ 5.95.

XX **Busabong Too,** 1a Langton St., SW1D 0JL, ℰ 352 7517, Thai rest. – ⬛. ⬛ ⟪ℰ⟫ ⓞ *VISA* — FZ **x**
closed Bank Holiday lunch and 24 to 27 December – **M** (booking essential) 14.95/19.50 **t.** and a la carte.

XX **Nakano,** 11 Beauchamp Pl., SW3 1NQ, ℰ 581 3837, Japanese rest. – ⬛. ⬛ ⟪ℰ⟫ ⓞ *VISA* — ER **r**
closed Sunday lunch, Monday, Easter, 1 week August and 23 December-6 January – **M** 18.00/42.50 **t.** and a la carte.

XX Sandrini, 260-262a Brompton Rd, SW3 2AS, ℰ 584 1724, Italian rest. — DS **n**

XX **Poissonnerie de l'Avenue,** 82 Sloane Av., SW3 3DZ, ℰ 589 2457, Fax 581 3360, French Seafood rest. – ⬛. ⬛ ⟪ℰ⟫ ⓞ *VISA* — DS **u**
closed Sunday, 24 December-3 January, Easter and Bank Holidays – **M** a la carte 20.25/ 27.25 **t.** ⟨ 4.50.

XX **St. Quentin,** 243 Brompton Rd, SW3 2EP, ℰ 589 8005, Fax 584 6064, French rest. – ⬛. ⬛ ⟪ℰ⟫ ⓞ *VISA* — DR **a**
M 12.50/15.25 **t.** and a la carte ⟨ 5.10.

XX Penang, 294 Fulham Rd, SW10 9EW, ℰ 351 2599, Malaysian rest. – ⬛. — BU **e**

XX Eleven Park Walk, 11 Park Walk, SW10 0PZ, ℰ 352 3449, Italian rest. – ⬛ — CU **r**

XX **Magic Dragon**, 99-103 Fulham Rd, SW3 6RH, ☎ 225 2244, Fax 929 5689, Chinese res
🔲. 🔼 🗚 ⑩ *VISA*
closed Monday and Bank Holidays – **M** 10.00/28.00 **st.** and a la carte.
DS

XX **Good Earth**, 233 Brompton Rd, SW3 2EP, ☎ 584 3658, Fax 823 8769, Chinese rest. –
🔼 🗚 ⑩ *VISA*
closed 24 to 27 December – **M** 10.00/25.00 **t.** and a la carte ⱡ 3.50.
DR

XX **Good Earth**, 91 King's Rd, SW3 4PA, ☎ 352 9231, Chinese rest. – 🔲. 🔼 🗚 ⑩ *VISA*
M 11.50/30.00 **t.** and a la carte ⱡ 3.50.
EU

XX **Toto's**, Walton House, Walton St., SW3 2JH, ☎ 589 0075, Italian rest. – 🔼
VISA
ES
closed 2 days at Easter and 3 days at Christmas – **M** 18.00/25.00 **st.** and a la carte ⱡ 6

XX **Beccofino**, 100 Draycott Av., SW3 3AD, ☎ 584 3600, Italian rest. – 🔼 🗚 *VISA*
ES
closed Sunday – **M** a la carte 14.90/28.10 ⱡ 3.70.

XX **Le Suquet**, 104 Draycott Av., SW3 3AE, ☎ 581 1785, French Seafood rest. – 🔼 🗚
VISA
DS
M a la carte approx. 21.00 **t.**

XX **Dan's**, 119 Sydney St., SW3 6NR, ☎ 352 2718, Fax 352 3265 – 🔼 🗚 ⑩ *VISA*
DU
closed Saturday lunch, Sunday, Christmas-New Year and Bank Holidays – **M** 22.0
(dinner) and a la carte ⱡ 4.50.

X **Ziani**, 45-47 Radnor Walk, SW3 4BP, ☎ 351 5297, Italian rest. – 🔼 🗚 ⑩ *VISA*
EU
M 20.00/25.00 **t.** and a la carte ⱡ 4.25.

X **Ma Cuisine**, 113 Walton St., SW3 2HP, ☎ 584 7585, French rest.
DS
closed Sunday and Bank Holidays – **M** (booking essential) 21.00 **s.** (lunch) and a
carte 18.45/29.65 ⱡ 8.50.

X **Thierry's**, 342 King's Rd, SW3 5UR, ☎ 352 3365 – 🔼 🗚 ⑩ *VISA*
CU
closed Sunday dinner, Easter, 17 to 30 August and Bank Holidays – **M** 9.90/32.00 **st.** an
la carte ⱡ 4.50.

X **The Wilds**, 356 Fulham Rd, SW10 9UH, ☎ 376 5553 – 🔲.
FZ

X **Monkey's**, 1 Cale St., Chelsea Green, SW3 3QT, ☎ 352 4711 – 🔲. 🔼 *VISA*
ET
closed Saturday, Sunday, 2 weeks Easter, 3 weeks August and 2 days at Christmas –
15.00/30.00 **t.** and a la carte ⱡ 5.50.

X **Beit Eddine**, 8 Harriet St., SW1 9JW, ☎ 235 3969, Lebanese rest.
FQ

Earl's Court – ⊠ SW5/SW10 – 🕿 071 – Except where otherwise stated see pp. 30-

🏨 **Burns Park**, Barkston Gdns, SW5 0EN, ☎ 373 3151, Telex 27885, Fax 370 4090 – 📳 📺
106 rm.
AT

🏨 **Rushmore** without rest., 11 Trebovir Rd, SW5 9LS, ☎ 370 3839, Fax 370 0274 – 📺 ☎
🔼 🗚 ⑩ *VISA*. ✄
p. 24 EZ
22 rm ⊇ 39.00/79.00 **st.**

🏨 **Amsterdam** without rest., 7 Trebovir Rd, SW5 9LS, ☎ 370 2814, Fax 244 7608 – 📳 📺
🔼 🗚 *VISA*
p. 24 EZ
20 rm ⊇ 39.00/51.00 **st.**

XX **Tiger Lee**, 251 Old Brompton Rd, SW5 9HP, ☎ 370 3176, Chinese Seafood rest
🔲
AU

XX **La Primula**, 12 Kenway Rd, SW5 0RR, ☎ 370 5958, Italian rest. – 🔼 🗚 ⑩ *VISA*
M 16.50 **t.** and a la carte ⱡ 3.50.
p. 24 FZ

X **Formula Veneta**, 14 Hollywood Rd, SW10 9HY, ☎ 352 7612, Italian rest.
BU

X **Left Bank**, 88 Ifield Rd, SW10 9AD, ☎ 352 0970 – 🔲. 🔼 *VISA*
p. 24 FZ
closed Sunday dinner – **M** (dinner only and Sunday lunch) a la carte 16.50/26.80 **t.** ⱡ 2.80

Kensington – ⊠ SW7/W8/W11/W14 – 🕿 071 – Except where otherwise stated s
pp. 24-27.

🏨🏨 **Royal Garden** (Rank), Kensington High St., W8 4PT, ☎ 937 8000, Telex 2631
Fax 938 4532, < Kensington Gardens – 📳 ⇄ rm 🔲 📺 ☎ 🅟 – 🛗 800. 🔼 🗚 ⑩ *VISA*. ✄
M Royal Roof (*closed Saturday lunch and Sunday*) (*dancing Saturday night*) 18.95/33.00
and a la carte ⱡ 7.50 – ⊇ 11.95 – **383 rm** 175.00/195.00 **st.**, **15 suites** 275.00/950.00 **st**
SB (weekends only) 132.00/154.00 **st.**
p. 30 AQ

🏨🏨 **Halcyon**, 81 Holland Park, W11 3RZ, ☎ 727 7288, Telex 266721, Fax 229 8516 – 📳 🔲
☎. 🔼 🗚 ⑩ *VISA*. ✄
EX
M – Kingfisher a la carte 12.50/21.75 **t.** ⱡ 6.50 – ⊇ 12.50 – **41 rm** 165.00/235.00 **st.**, **3 sui**
250.00/550.00 **st.** – SB (weekends only) 195.00 **st.**

🏨🏨 **Copthorne Tara** (Best Western), Scarsdale Pl., W8 5SR, ☎ 937 7211, Telex 9188
Fax 937 7100 – 📳 ⇄ rm 🔲 📺 ☎ ♿ 🅟 – 🛗 500. 🔼 🗚 ⑩ *VISA*. ✄
FY
M 12.15/22.50 **st.** and a la carte ⱡ 8.40 – ⊇ 8.95 – **820 rm** 99.00/140.00 **st.**, **8 sui**
235.00/355.00 **st.**

🏨🏨 **London Kensington Hilton**, 179-199 Holland Park Av., W11 4UL, ☎ 603 3355, Tel
919763, Fax 602 9397 – 📳 ⇄ rm 🔲 📺 ☎ ♿ 🅟 – 🛗 200. 🔼 🗚 ⑩ *VISA*. ✄
EX
M (carving lunch) 18.95/35.00 **st.** and a la carte ⱡ 5.50 – (see also **Hiroko** below) – ⊇ 11
– **596 rm** 108.00/165.00 **st.**, **7 suites** 230.00/300.00 **st.**

Kensington Park, 16-32 De Vere Gardens, W8 5AG, ℰ 937 8080, Telex 929643, Fax 937 7616 – 📶 📺 ☎ ♿ – 🔬 120. 🅰 AE ⑩ VISA ⌘
M 13.80 **t.** and a la carte § 5.40 – ⊑ 9.95 – **325 rm** 99.00/120.00 **st., 7 suites** 240.00/275.00 **st.**
BQ **e**

Kensington Palace Thistle (Mt. Charlotte Thistle), 8 De Vere Gdns, W8 5AF, ℰ 937 8121, Telex 262422, Fax 937 2816 – 📶 ↔ rm 🍴 rest 📺 ☎ – 🔬 180. 🅰 AE ⑩ VISA ⌘
p. 30 BQ **a**
M 10.50/17.00 **st.** and a la carte § 6.95 – ⊑ 9.95 – **297 rm** 95.00/130.00 **st., 1 suite** 250.00 **st.** – SB 119.00/217.00 **st.**

Kensington Close (Forte), Wrights Lane, W8 5SP, ℰ 937 8170, Fax 937 8289, ⅙, ⓢ, ⎙, ☞, squash – 📶 ↔ rm 🍴 rest 📺 ☎ 🅿 – 🔬 150. 🅰 AE ⑩ VISA
FY **c**
M 14.25 **t.** and a la carte § 5.00 – ⊑ 7.50 – **530 rm** 85.00/95.00 **st.** – SB 98.00 **st.**

Holland Court without rest., 31 Holland Rd, W14 8HJ, ℰ 371 1133, Fax 602 9114, ☞ – 📶 📺 ☎
EY **e**
24 rm.

Russell Court without rest., 9 Russell Rd, W14 8JA, ℰ 603 1222, Fax 371 2286 – 📶 📺 ☎. 🅰 AE VISA ⌘
EY **v**
18 rm 59.50/69.50 **st.**

London Lodge, 134-136 Lexham Gdns, W8 6JE, ℰ 244 8444, Telex 922921, Fax 373 6661 – 📶 📺 ☎. 🅰 AE ⑩ VISA
EYZ **r**
M 13.50 **t.** § 3.50 – ⊑ 8.95 – **27 rm** 77.00/198.00 **st.**

🅇🅇 **Belvedere in Holland Park,** Holland House, off Abbotsbury Rd, W8 6LU, ℰ 602 1238 – « 19C orangery in park » 🍴. 🅰 AE ⑩ VISA
EY **u**
closed Saturday lunch, Sunday dinner and 25 December – M (booking essential) a la carte 16.10/23.60 **t.**

🅇 **Clarke's,** 124 Kensington Church St., W8 4BH, ℰ 221 9225, Fax 229 4564 – 🍴. 🅰 VISA
EX **c**

🅇 **La Pomme d'Amour,** 128 Holland Park Av., W11 4UE, ℰ 229 8532, French rest. – 🍴. 🅰 AE ⑩ VISA
EX **e**
closed Saturday lunch, Sunday and Bank Holidays – M 12.50/19.50 **t.** and a la carte § 4.50.

🅇 **L'Escargot Doré,** 2-4 Thackeray St., W8 5ET, ℰ 937 8508, French rest. – 🍴. 🅰 AE ⑩ VISA
AR **e**
closed Saturday lunch, Sunday, last 2 weeks August and Bank Holidays – M 13.90 **t.** and a la carte § 4.80.

🅇 **Shanghai,** 38c-d Kensington Church St., W8 4BX, ℰ 938 2501, Chinese rest. – 🍴. 🅰 AE ⑩ VISA
FX **a**
closed 24 to 26 December and Bank Holidays – M 16.50/23.00 **t.** and a la carte § 4.00.

🅇 **La Fenice,** 148 Holland Park Av., W11 4UE, ℰ 221 6090, Italian rest. – 🍴. 🅰 AE VISA
EX **v**
closed Saturday lunch, Monday and Bank Holidays – M 11.50 **t.** and a la carte § 3.20.

🅇 **Launceston Place,** la Launceston Pl., W8 5RL, ℰ 937 6912, Fax 938 2412 – 🍴. 🅰 VISA
p. 30 BR **a**
closed Saturday lunch and Sunday dinner – M 14.95 **t.** (lunch) and a la carte 21.00/26.00 **t.** § 4.00.

🅇 **Hiroko** (at London Kensington Hilton H.), 179-199 Holland Park Av., W11 4UL, ℰ 603 5003, Japanese rest. – 🅿. 🅰 AE ⑩ VISA
EX **s**

🅇 **Princess Garden,** 11 Russell Gdns, WI4 8EZ, ℰ 602 0312, Chinese rest. – 🍴
EY **i**

🅇 **Phoenicia,** 11-13 Abingdon Rd, W8 6AH, ℰ 937 0120, Lebanese rest. – 🍴. 🅰 AE ⑩ VISA
EY **n**
closed 25 and 26 December – M 8.95/26.20 **st.** and a la carte.

🅇 **Boyd's,** 135 Kensington Church St., W8 7LP, ℰ 727 5452 – 🅰 AE VISA
p. 32 AZ **r**
M 14.85 **t.** (lunch) and a la carte 19.25/32.45 **t.** § 6.75.

🅇 **La Paesana,** 30 Uxbridge St., W8 7TA, ℰ 229 4332, Italian rest. – 🍴. AE ⑩ VISA
p. 32 AZ **i**
closed Sunday, Easter and Bank Holidays – M a la carte 13.90/16.40 **t.** § 3.80.

🅇🅇 **Sailing Junk,** 59 Marloes Rd, W8 6LE, ℰ 937 2589, Chinese rest. – 🍴. 🅰 AE ⑩ VISA
FY **x**
closed Sunday lunch – M 4.80/19.80 **st.** and a la carte § 3.50.

🅇 **I Ching,** 40 Earls Court Rd, W8 6EJ, ℰ 937 0409, Chinese (Peking, Szechuan) rest. – 🍴
EY **u**

🅇 **Kensington Place,** 201 Kensington Church St., W8 7LX, ℰ 727 3184, Fax 229 2025 – 🍴. 🅰 VISA
p. 32 AZ **z**
M 12.50 **t.** (lunch) and a la carte 15.00/24.50 **t.** § 4.00.

🅇 **Café Kensington,** 2 Lancer Sq., Kensington Church St., W8 4EH, ℰ 938 2211 – 🍴. 🅰 AE ⑩ VISA
AQ **u**
closed Bank Holidays – M a la carte 13.00/20.00 **t.** § 3.75.

🅇 **Cibo,** 3 Russell Gdns, W14 8EZ, ℰ 371 6271, Italian rest. – ⭐ AE ⑩ VISA
EY **o**
closed Sunday dinner – M a la carte 17.00/38.90 **t.** § 4.75.

🅇 **Malabar,** 27 Uxbridge St., W8 7TQ, ℰ 727 8800, Indian rest. – 🅰 VISA
p. 32 AZ **e**
closed 31 August-6 September and 25 to 27 December – M (buffet lunch Sunday) a la carte 13.70/17.95 **st.** § 4.50.

X **The Ark,** Kensington Court, 35 Kensington High St., W8 5BA, ℰ 937 4294, French res
🔤 🔤 🔤 🔤 p. 30 AQ
closed lunch Sunday and Bank Holidays and 4 days at Christmas – **M** a la carte 13
20.80 **t.** ▮ 3.25.

X **Café Francais,** 6 Holland St., W8 4LT, ℰ 937 3367 – 🔤 🔤 🔤 FY
closed 25-26 December and 1 January – **M** 19.45 **t.** and a la carte.

X **Wódka,** 12 St. Albans Grove, W8 5PN, ℰ 937 6513, Polish rest. – 🔤 🔤 🔤 AR
closed lunch Saturday and Sunday – **M** a la carte 14.40/20.40 **t.** ▮ 3.90.

X Mandarin, 197c Kensington High St., W8 6BA, ℰ 937 1551, Chinese rest. – 🔤 EY

North Kensington – ⊠ W2/W10/W11 – ✆ 071 – Except where otherwise stated
pp. 20-23.

🏨 **Abbey Court** without rest., 20 Pembridge Gdns, W2 4DU, ℰ 221 7518, Telex 2621
Fax 792 0858, « Tastefully furnished Victorian town house » – 🔤 ☎. 🔤 🔤 🔤 🔤.
⊆ 7.00 – **22 rm** 84.00/150.00 **t.** p. 32 AZ

🏨 **Pembridge Court,** 34 Pembridge Gdns, W2 4DX, ℰ 229 9977, Telex 2983
Fax 727 4982 – 🕻 🔤 rest 🔤 rest 🔤 ☎. 🔤 🔤 🔤 🔤 p. 32 AZ
M *(closed Sunday and Bank Holidays)* (dinner only) a la carte 12.00/18.50 **t.** ▮ 4.80 – **25**
⊆ 65.00/110.00 **s.**

🏨 **Portobello,** 22 Stanley Gdns, W11 2NG, ℰ 727 2777, Telex 268349, Fax 792 9641, «
tractive town house in Victorian terrace » – 🕻 🔤 ☎. 🔤 🔤 🔤 🔤 🔤 EV
closed 23 December-2 January – **M** (residents only) 15.00/20.00 **st.** and a la carte ▮ 4.8
⊆ 6.95 – **24 rm** 70.50/125.73 **st.** **1 suite** 170.38 **st.**

🏨 Holland Park without rest., 6 Ladbroke Terr., W11 3PG, ℰ 792 0216, Fax 727 8166, 🚗 –
☎ – **23 rm.** EX

XXX **Leith's,** 92 Kensington Park Rd, W11 2PN, ℰ 229 4481 – 🔤. 🔤 🔤 🔤 EV
closed 30-31 August and 24 to 27 December – **M** (dinner only) 23.50/44.00 **st.** ▮ 6.75.

XX **Chez Moi,** 1 Addison Av., Holland Park, W11 4QS, ℰ 603 8267, French rest. – 🔤 🔤
🔤 p. 24 EX
closed Saturday lunch, Sunday, Christmas-New Year and Bank Holidays – **M** 14.0
(lunch) and a la carte 18.25/27.25 **t.** ▮ 4.75.

X **Canal Brasserie,** Canalot Studios, 222 Kensal Rd, W10 5BN, ℰ 960 2732 – 🔤 🔤
closed Saturday and Sunday – **M** a la carte approx. 17.00 **t.** ET

South Kensington – ⊠ SW5/SW7/W8 – ✆ 071 – Except where otherwise stated
pp. 30 and 31.

🏨 **Blakes,** 33 Roland Gdns, SW7 3PF, ℰ 370 6701, Telex 8813500, Fax 373 0442, « Anti
oriental furnishings » – 🕻 🔤 rest 🔤 ☎. 🔤 🔤 🔤 🔤 BU
M 28.50 **st.** (lunch) and a la carte 31.75/53.50 **t.** ▮ 7.00 – ⊆ 14.50 – **46 rm** 150.00/270.00
6 suites 220.00/600.00 **t.**

🏨 **Pelham,** 15 Cromwell Pl., SW7 2LA, ℰ 589 8288, Telex 8814714, Fax 584 8444, « Tas
fully furnished Victorian town house » – 🕻 🔤 rest 🔤 ☎. 🔤 🔤 🔤 🔤 CS
M 14.95/17.95 **st.** and a la carte ▮ 9.50 – **34 rm** ⊆ 115.00/165.00 **t.** **3 suites** 200.
265.00 **t.**

🏨 **Gloucester** (Rank), 4-19 Harrington Gdns, SW7 4LH, ℰ 373 6030, Telex 9175
Fax 370 0409 – 🕻 🔤 rm 🔤 🔤 ☎. 🔤 🔤 400. 🔤 🔤 🔤 🔤 🔤 BS
M 21.40 **st.** (dinner) and a la carte 19.95/33.25 **t.** ▮ 8.00 – ⊆ 11.50 – **544 rm** 150.
180.00 **st.** **6 suites** 210.00/750.00 **st.**

🏨 **Rembrandt,** 11 Thurloe Pl., SW7 2RS, ℰ 589 8100, Telex 295828, Fax 225 3363, 🏋,
🔤 – 🕻 🔤 rm 🔤 rest 🔤 ☎ – 🔤 250. 🔤 🔤 🔤 🔤 DS
M 16.75 **st.** and a la carte ▮ 6.50 – ⊆ 9.20 – **196 rm** 97.00/260.00 **st.** – SB (weekends o
127.90/147.90 **st.**

🏨 **Swallow International,** Cromwell Rd, SW5 0TH, ℰ 973 1000, Telex 272
Fax 244 8194, 🏋, 🏊, 🔤 – 🕻 🔤 rm 🔤 rest 🔤 ☎ 🅿 – 🔤 200. 🔤 🔤 🔤 🔤 🔤 AS
closed 3 days at Christmas – **M** 15.00/20.00 **st.** and a la carte ▮ 6.00 – ⊆ 8.25 – **415**
95.00/120.00 **st.** **1 suite** 150.00/250.00 **st.** – SB 183.00/240.00 **st.**

🏨 **Holiday Inn,** 94-106 Cromwell Rd, SW7 4ER, ℰ 373 2222, Telex 911311, Fax 373 05
🏋, 🏊 🔤 🔤 ☎ – 🔤 125. 🔤 🔤 🔤 🔤 BS
M 9.95/15.95 **t.** and a la carte – ⊆ 10.95 – **143 rm** 118.00/145.00 **st.** **19 suites** 190.
250.00 **st.** – SB (weekends only) 94.00/112.00 **st.**

🏨 **Gore** (Best Western), 189 Queen's Gate, SW7 5EX, ℰ 584 6601, Telex 2962
Fax 589 8127, « Attractive decor » – 🕻 🔤 ☎. 🔤 🔤 🔤 🔤 🔤 BR
M (only members and residents may book) a la carte 12.25/20.80 – ⊆ 9.40 – **58**
87.00/109.00 **s.**

🏨 **Regency,** 100 Queen's Gate, SW7 5AG, ℰ 370 4595, Telex 267594, Fax 370 5555, 🏋,
– 🕻 🔤 rm 🔤 rest 🔤 ☎ – 🔤 100. 🔤 🔤 🔤 🔤 CT
M *(closed lunch Saturday and Sunday)* 15.00/25.00 **st.** and a la carte – ⊆ 12.00 – **204**
111.00/131.00 **st.** **6 suites** 190.00/225.00 **st.** – SB (weekends only) 140.00/180.00 **st.**

🏨 **John Howard** (Best Western), 4 Queen's Gate, SW7 5EH, ℰ 581 3011, Telex 88133
Fax 589 8403 – 🕻 🔤 🔤 ☎. 🔤 🔤 🔤 🔤 BQ
M 15.75 **st.** and a la carte ▮ 4.50 – ⊆ 9.75 – **52 rm** 85.00/175.00 **st.**

🏨 **Onslow,** 109-113 Queen's Gate, SW7 5LR, ☎ 589 6300, Telex 262180, Fax 581 1492 – 🛗
🍽 rest 📺 ☎ – 🔬 80. 🔼 ᴁᴇ ⓞ 𝘷𝘪𝘴𝘢 CT i
M 13.50/15.00 t. and a la carte ≬ 5.00 – ⌑ 8.50 – **173 rm** 99.00/125.00 t.

🏨 **Bailey's,** 140 Gloucester Rd, SW7 4QH, ☎ 373 6000, Telex 264221, Fax 370 3760 – 🛗 📺
☎ – 🔬 70. 🔼 ᴁᴇ ⓞ 𝘷𝘪𝘴𝘢. ⌑ BS a
⌑ 11.00 – **162 rm** 140.00/450.00 t.

🏨 **Cranley** without rest., 8-12 Bina Gardens, SW5 0LA, ☎ 373 0123, Fax 373 9497, « Tasteful decor, antiques » – 🛗 📺 ☎. 🔼 ᴁᴇ ⓞ 𝘷𝘪𝘴𝘢 BT c
⌑ 11.45 – **31 rm** 99.00/160.00 st., **4 suites** 205.00/277.00 st.

🏨 **Vanderbilt** (Edwardian), 68-86 Cromwell Rd, SW7 5BT, ☎ 589 2424, Telex 946944,
Fax 225 2293 – 🛗 🍽 rest 📺 ☎ – 🔬 120 BS v
223 rm.

🏨 **Park International,** 117/125 Cromwell Rd, SW7 4DS, ☎ 370 5711, Telex 296822,
Fax 244 9211 – 🛗 📺 ☎ – 🔬 45 AS e
117 rm.

🏨 **Embassy House** (Jarvis), 31-33 Queen's Gate, SW7 5JA, ☎ 584 7222, Telex 914893,
Fax 589 8193 – 🛗 📺 ☎. 🔼 ᴁᴇ ⓞ 𝘷𝘪𝘴𝘢 BR e
M *(closed lunch Saturday and Sunday)* (buffet lunch)/dinner 22.00 t. and a la carte – **67 rm**,
1 suite.

🏨 **Norfolk** (Q.M.H.), 2-10 Harrington Rd, SW7 3ER, ☎ 589 8191, Telex 268852,
Fax 581 1874, 𝘍ₐ, ≦ₛ – 🛗 📺 ☎ – 🔬 60. 🔼 ᴁᴇ ⓞ 𝘷𝘪𝘴𝘢. ⌑ CS e
M (see Brasserie de la Paix below) – ⌑ 9.00 – **93 rm** 115.00/145.00 st., **3 suites** 165.00/
185.00 st. – SB 130.00 st.

🏨 **Kensington Plaza,** 61 Gloucester Rd, SW7 4PE, ☎ 584 8100, Telex 8950993,
Fax 823 9915, ≦ₛ – 🛗 📺 ☎ – 🔬 50. 🔼 ᴁᴇ ⓞ 𝘷𝘪𝘴𝘢 BS e
M (Indian rest.) 15.00/20.00 st. and a la carte ≬ 7.95 – ⌑ 7.50 – **90 rm** 70.00/120.00 st.

🏛 **Number Sixteen** without rest., 14-17 Sumner Pl., SW7 3EG, ☎ 589 5232, Telex 266638,
Fax 584 8615, « Attractively furnished Victorian town houses », 🌿 – 🛗 📺 ☎. 🔼 ᴁᴇ ⓞ
𝘷𝘪𝘴𝘢. ⌑ CT c
⌑ 8.00 **36 rm** 60.00/160.00 t.

🏛 Cranley Place without rest., 1 Cranley Pl., SW7 3AB, ☎ 589 7944, Fax 225 3931, « Tasteful
decor » – 📺 ☎. 🔼 ᴁᴇ ⓞ 𝘷𝘪𝘴𝘢 CT o
10 rm.

🏛 **Five Sumner Place** without rest., 5 Sumner Place, SW7 3EE, ☎ 584 7586, Fax 823 9962
– 🛗 📺 ☎. 🔼 ᴁᴇ ⓞ 𝘷𝘪𝘴𝘢. ⌑ CT a
13 rm ⌑ 55.00/95.00 st.

🏛 **Cranley Gardens** without rest., 8 Cranley Gdns, SW7 3DB, ☎ 373 3232, Telex 894489,
Fax 373 7944 – 🛗 📺 ☎. 🔼 ᴁᴇ ⓞ 𝘷𝘪𝘴𝘢 BT e
⌑ 5.50 – **85 rm** 63.00/89.00 st.

🏛 **Alexander** without rest., 9 Sumner Pl., SW7 3EE, ☎ 581 1591, Telex 917133,
Fax 581 0824, « Attractively furnished Victorian town houses », 🌿 – 🛗 📺 ☎. 🔼 ᴁᴇ ⓞ
𝘷𝘪𝘴𝘢. ⌑ CT a
36 rm ⌑ 85.00/155.00, **1 suite** 195.00.

🏛 **Aster House** without rest., 3 Sumner Pl., SW7 3EE, ☎ 581 5888, Fax 584 4925, 🌿 – ✍
📺 ☎. 🔼 ᴁᴇ ⓞ 𝘷𝘪𝘴𝘢. ⌑ CT u
12 rm ⌑ 52.00/79.00 s.

✕✕ **Bombay Brasserie,** Courtfield Close, 140 Gloucester Rd, SW7 4QH, ☎ 370 4040, Indian
rest., « Raj-style decor, conservatory garden » – 🍽. 🔼 𝘷𝘪𝘴𝘢 BS a
closed 25 and 26 December – **M** (buffet lunch) 13.50 t. and dinner a la carte approx. 17.30 t.
≬ 4.95.

✕ **Hilaire,** 68 Old Brompton Rd, SW7 3LQ, ☎ 584 8993 – 🍽. 🔼 ᴁᴇ ⓞ 𝘷𝘪𝘴𝘢 CT n
closed Sunday, 1 week Easter, 2 weeks August, 1 week Christmas and Bank Holidays – **M**
(booking essential) 20.95/34.00 t. and a la carte 29.50/37.00 t. ≬ 7.00.

✕ **Brasserie de la Paix** (at Norfolk H.), 10 Harrington Rd, SW7 3ER, ☎ 589 8191, Telex
268852, Fax 581 1874 – 🍽. 🔼 ᴁᴇ ⓞ 𝘷𝘪𝘴𝘢 CS e
M *(closed Saturday lunch)* 11.95/18.00 t. and a la carte ≬ 6.50.

✕ Nizam, 152 Old Brompton Rd, SW5 0BE, ☎ 373 0024, Indian rest. – 🍽 BT a

✕ **Mr Wing,** 242-244 Old Brompton Rd, SW5 0DE, ☎ 370 4450, Chinese rest. – ✍. 🔼 ᴁᴇ
ⓞ 𝘷𝘪𝘴𝘢 AV a
closed 25 to 30 December – **M** 15.00/20.00 t. and a la carte.

✕ **Tui,** 19 Exhibition Rd, SW7 2HE, ☎ 584 8359, Fax 352 8343, Thai rest. – 🔼 ᴁᴇ ⓞ 𝘷𝘪𝘴𝘢
closed Bank Holidays – **M** a la carte 12.15/20.05 t. CS u

✕ **Delhi Brasserie,** 134 Cromwell Rd, SW7 4HA, ☎ 370 7617, Indian rest. – 🍽. 🔼 ᴁᴇ ⓞ
𝘷𝘪𝘴𝘢 AS a
closed 25 and 26 December – **M** 14.25 t. and a la carte.

✕ **Memories of India,** 18 Gloucester Rd, SW7 4RB, ☎ 589 6450, Telex 265196,
Fax 581 5980, Indian rest. – 🍽. 🔼 ᴁᴇ ⓞ 𝘷𝘪𝘴𝘢 BR s
closed 25 and 26 December – **M** 14.50/15.00 t. and a la carte.

✗ **Chanterelle,** 119 Old Brompton Rd, SW7 3RN, ℘ 373 5522 – 🖾 🗚 ⓞ 𝘝𝘐𝘚𝘈   BT
closed 25 to 28 December – **M** 11.50/19.00 **t.** ⓵ 5.50.

✗ **Gilberts,** 2 Exhibition Rd, SW7 2HP, ℘ 589 8947 – 🖾 🗚 ⓞ 𝘝𝘐𝘚𝘈   CS
closed Saturday lunch, Sunday and last 2 weeks August – **M** 16.50/21.50 **t.** ⓵ 4.45.

✗ **Nam Long at Le Shaker,** 159 Old Brompton Rd, SW5 0LJ, ℘ 373 1926, Vietname
rest. – 🖾 🗚 ⓞ 𝘝𝘐𝘚𝘈   BT
closed Saturday lunch, Sunday and Bank Holidays – **M** 15.00/30.00 **st.** and a la carte.

✗ **Bangkok,** 9 Bute St., SW7 3EY, ℘ 584 8529, Thai bistro – ▤. 🖾 🗚 𝘝𝘐𝘚𝘈   CS
closed Sunday, 1 week August and Bank Holidays – **M** a la carte 18.00/22.50 **t.**

KINGSTON UPON THAMES pp. 9 and 10.

🖪 Hampton Wick ℘ (081) 977 6645, by A 308 – 🖪 Coombe Wood, George Rd ℘ (081) 942 38
NE : 1¼ m. on A 308.

🖪 Museum & Heritage Centre, Wheatfield Way ℘ (081) 546 5386.

Chessington – ✉ Surrey – ☎ 0372.

🏛 **Travel Inn,** Leatherhead Rd, KT9 2NE, on A 243 ℘ 744060, Fax 720889 – ⇔ rm 📺 ȼ
🖾 🗚 ⓞ 𝘝𝘐𝘚𝘈. ⅏   BZ
M (Beefeater grill) a la carte approx. 13.50 **t.** – ⌁ 4.50 – **42 rm** 31.00 **t.**

Kingston – ✉ Surrey – ☎ 081.

🖪 Malden, Traps Lane ℘ 942 0654.

🏨 **Kingston Lodge** (Forte), Kingston Hill, KT2 7NP, ℘ 541 4481, Telex 936034, Fax 547 10
– ⇔ rm 📺 ☎ ȼ 🄿 – 🕍 60. 🖾 🗚 ⓞ 𝘝𝘐𝘚𝘈   CY
M (bar lunch Saturday) 14.50/18.00 **st.** and a la carte ⓵ 4.05 – ⌁ 8.15 – **62 rm** 85.0
135.00 **st.** – SB (weekends only) 98.00 **st.**

✗✗ **Gravier,** 9 Station Rd, Norbiton, KT2 7AA, ℘ 549 5557, French Seafood rest. – 🖾 🗚
𝘝𝘐𝘚𝘈   CY
closed Saturday lunch, Sunday, 1 week Easter, last 2 weeks August and 1 week Christma
M 14.50 **t.** (lunch) and a la carte 20.15/26.90 **t.** ⓵ 4.25.

✗ **Ayudhya,** 14 Kingston Hill, KT2 7NH, ℘ 549 5984, Thai rest. – 🖾 🗚 ⓞ 𝘝𝘐𝘚𝘈   CY
closed Saturday lunch, 19 April, 25-26 December and 1 January – **M** a la carte 8.80/11.3
⓵ 3.45.

✗ **Lemongrass,** 54 Fife Rd, KT1 1SU, ℘ 546 8221, Thai rest. – 🖾 𝘝𝘐𝘚𝘈   CY
closed Sunday and Bank Holidays – **M** 6.00/10.00 **t.** and a la carte ⓵ 4.85.

Surbiton – ✉ Surrey – ☎ 081.

🖪 Woodstock Lane, Chessington ℘ 398 3101, S : 3½ m. by A 243.

✗✗ **Chez Max,** 85 Maple Rd, KT6 4AW, ℘ 399 2365 – 🖾 🗚 ⓞ 𝘝𝘐𝘚𝘈   BY
closed Saturday lunch, Sunday, Monday, 26 December and 1 January – **M** (book
essential) 18.50/27.00 **t.** and a la carte ⓵ 6.50.

LAMBETH Except where otherwise stated see pp.10 and 11.

Brixton – ✉ SW9 – ☎ 071.

✗ **Twenty Trinity Gardens,** 20 Trinity Gdns, SW9 8DP, ℘ 733 8838 – 🖾 𝘝𝘐𝘚𝘈   EX
closed Saturday lunch, Sunday dinner and 25 to 30 December – **M** 11.75/16.75 **t.** ⓵ 4.25

Clapham Common – ✉ SW4 – ☎ 071.

✗✗ **The Grafton,** 45 Old Town, SW4 0JL, ℘ 627 1048, French rest. – 🖾 🗚 ⓞ 𝘝𝘐𝘚𝘈
closed Saturday lunch, Sunday, last 3 weeks August and Bank Holidays – **M** 26.
30.00 **t.** and a la carte ⓵ 5.50.   p. 13 DQ

Streatham – ✉ SW16 – ☎ 081.

⌂ **Barrow House** without rest., 45 Barrow Rd, SW16 5PE, ℘ 677 1925, « Victoriana », ⅏
⇔. ⅏   EY
5 rm ⌁ 16.00/30.00 **st.**

Waterloo – ✉ SE1 – ☎ 071.

✗✗ **La Rive Gauche,** 61 The Cut, SE1 8LL, ℘ 928 8645, French rest. – 🖾 🗚 ⓞ 𝘝𝘐𝘚𝘈
closed Saturday lunch, Sunday and Bank Holidays – **M** 17.50 **st.** and a la carte ⓵ 5.50.
p. 27 NX

✗✗ **RSJ,** 13a Coin St., SE1 8YQ, ℘ 928 4554 – ▤. 🖾 🗚 𝘝𝘐𝘚𝘈   p. 27 NX
closed Saturday lunch, Sunday and Bank Holidays – **M** 13.75/15.25 **t.** and a la carte ⓵ 5.

LONDON HEATHROW AIRPORT see Hillingdon, London p. 61.

ERTON pp. 8 and 9.

Wimbledon – ⊠ SW19 – ✆ 081.

₧ London Scottish, Windmill Enclosure ✆ 788 0135 – ₧ Wimbledon Common, Camp Rd ✆ 946 0294 – ₧ Home Park Rd, Wimbledon Park ✆ 946 1002 – ₧ Royal Wimbledon, 29 Camp Rd ✆ 946 2125.

Cannizaro House (Mt. Charlotte Thistle) ⍋, West Side, Wimbledon Common, SW19 4UF, ✆ 879 1464, Telex 9413837, Fax 879 7338, ≼, « 18C country house overlooking Cannizaro Park », ₧ – ⛔ 🆀 🖭 ❶ ❶ – ⚿ 40. ❰ 40. ❰❰❰ ❶ VISA   DXY **x**
M 28.00 st. and a la carte – ⊂⊃ 8.75 – **44 rm** 110.00/160.00 t., **2 suites** 210.00/285.00 t. – SB 160.00/250.00 st.

Worcester House without rest., 38 Alwyne Rd, SW19 7AE, ✆ 946 1300, Fax 785 4058 – 🖭 ☎. ❰❰ ❶ VISA   DY **r**
9 rm ⊂⊃ 44.65/65.50 t.

Bayee Village, 24 High St., SW19 5DX, ✆ 947 3533, Chinese (Peking, Szechuan) rest. – ▤. ❰❰ ❰❰❰ ❶ VISA   DX **i**
M 15.00 st. and a la carte ⌡ 6.00.

Wimbledon Palace, 88 The Broadway, SW19 1RH, ✆ 540 4505, Chinese (Peking, Szechuan) rest. – ▤. ❰❰ ❰❰❰ ❶ VISA   DY **e**
closed Saturday lunch and 25-26 December – **M** 7.95/20.00 t. and a la carte ⌡ 3.80.

Morden – ⊠ SM4 – ✆ 081.

Forte Travelodge without rest., Epsom Rd, SM4 5PH, SE : on A 24 ✆ 640 8227, Reservations (toll free) 0800 850950 – 🖭 ⚿ ❶. ❰❰ ❰❰❰ VISA. ⌦ – **32 rm** 29.95 t.   DY **c**

EDBRIDGE pp. 6 and 7.

Ilford – ⊠ Essex – ✆ 081.

₧ Wanstead Park Rd ✆ 554 5174, by A 12 – ₧ Fairlop Waters, Forest Rd, Barkingside ✆ 500 9911.

Mandarin Palace, 559-561 Cranbrook Rd, Gants Hill, IG2 6JZ, ✆ 550 7661, Chinese (Peking, Canton) rest. – ▤. ❰❰ ❰❰❰ ❶ VISA   HU **e**
M 9.50/16.00 st. and a la carte ⌡ 4.00.

Dragon City, 97 Cranbrook Rd, IG1 4PG, ✆ 553 0312, Chinese (Peking, Cantonese) rest. – ▤. ❰❰ ❰❰❰ ❶ VISA   JHU **a**
M 8.50/18.50 t. and a la carte.

South Woodford – ⊠ Essex – ✆ 081.

₧ Sunset Av., Woodford Green ✆ 504 0553.

Ho-Ho, 20 High Rd, E18 2QL, ✆ 989 1041, Chinese rest. – ▤. ❰❰ ❰❰❰ ❶ VISA   HU **c**
M 23.00 t. and a la carte.

Woodford – ⊠ Essex – ✆ 081.

Prince Regent, Manor Rd, Woodford Bridge, IG8 8AE, ✆ 505 9966, Fax 506 0807, ₧ – ⛔ ▤ rest 🖭 ☎ ⟺ ❶ – ⚿ 350. ❰❰ ❰❰❰ ❶ VISA   HT **a**
M 15.00/25.00 t. and a la carte ⌡ 5.50 – **51 rm** ⊂⊃ 75.00/125.00 st.

Woodford Moat House (Q.M.H.), 30 Oak Hill, Woodford Green, IG8 9NY, ✆ 505 4511, Telex 264428, Fax 506 0941, ₧ – ⛔ 🖭 ☎ ❶ – ⚿ 150. ❰❰ ❰❰❰ ❶ VISA ⌦   HT **c**
closed 26 December and 1 January – **M** (bar lunch Saturday) 14.80/25.00 t. and a la carte ⌡ 3.60 – **99 rm** ⊂⊃ 79.50/89.50 st. – SB (weekends only) 85.00 st.

CHMOND-UPON-THAMES pp. 8 and 9.

Barnes – ⊠ SW13 – ✆ 081.

Thurlow's, 5 White Hart Lane, SW13 0NT, ✆ 876 3335 – ❰❰ ❰❰❰ VISA   CX **r**
closed Saturday lunch, Sunday dinner, Monday and 2 weeks July-August – **M** 12.50 t. (lunch) and dinner a la carte 16.00/24.00 t. ⌡ 3.50.

Sonny's, 94 Church Rd, SW13 0DQ, ✆ 748 0393 – ▤. ❰❰ ❶ VISA   CX **x**
closed Sunday dinner, 1 week Christmas and Bank Holidays – **M** 11.95 t. and a la carte ⌡ 3.75.

Riva, 169 Church Rd, SW13 9HR, ✆ 748 0434, Italian rest. – ❰❰ VISA   CX **a**
closed Saturday lunch, Easter, 1 week Christmas and Bank Holidays – **M** a la carte 13.30/21.80 st. ⌡ 4.80.

East Sheen – ⊠ SW14 – ✆ 081.

Crowther's, 481 Upper Richmond Rd West, SW14 7PU, ✆ 876 6372 – ▤. ❰❰ ❰❰❰ VISA   CX **n**
closed lunch Monday and Saturday, Sunday, 2 weeks September, 1 week Christmas and Bank Holiday Mondays – **M** (booking essential) 16.50/22.00 t. and dinner a la carte ⌡ 4.50.

Richmond – ⊠ Surrey – ☎ 081.

🛚, 🛚 Richmond Park ℰ 876 3205 – 🛚 Sudbrook Park ℰ 940 1463 – 🛚, 🛚 Old Deer P
ℰ 940 1894 – 🖪 Old Town Hall, Whittaker Av. ℰ 940 9125, Fax 940 6899.

🏨 **Petersham** ⌘, Nightingale Lane, Richmond Hill, TW10 6UZ, ℰ 940 7471, Group Te
928556, Fax 940 9998, ≤, ☞ – ▮ 📺 ☎ 🅿 – 🔬 50. 🔼 🅰🅴 ⓞ 𝘝𝘐𝘚𝘈. ⌗
CX
M *(closed 24 to 26 December)* 19.00/22.00 **t.** and a la carte – **54 rm** ⊆ 100.00/155.00 s
SB (weekends only) 120.00/150.00 **st.**

🏨 **Richmond Gate** (Best Western), 158 Richmond Hill, TW10 6RP, ℰ 940 0061, Gre
Telex Fax 332 0354, ☞ – 📺 ☎ 🅿 – 🔬 40. 🔼 🅰🅴 ⓞ 𝘝𝘐𝘚𝘈. ⌗
CX
M (dinner only and Sunday lunch)/dinner 17.50 **st.** and a la carte ▯ 5.50 – **51 rm** ⊆ 85.
115.00 **st.** – SB (weekends only) 80.00/120.00 **st.**

🏨 **Bingham**, 61-63 Petersham Rd, TW10 6UT, ℰ 940 0902, Fax 948 8737, ☞ – 📺 ☎
🔬 30. 🔼 🅰🅴 ⓞ 𝘝𝘐𝘚𝘈. ⌗
CX
M *(closed Sunday)* (dinner only) 16.25 **t.** and a la carte ▯ 4.50 – **35 rm** ⊆ 70.00/100.00 s
SB (weekends only) 95.00/110.00 **st.**

🏨 **Richmond Park** without rest., 3 Petersham Rd, TW10 6UH, ℰ 948 4666, Fax 940 737
📺 ☎. 🔼 🅰🅴 ⓞ 𝘝𝘐𝘚𝘈. ⌗
CX
24 rm ⊆ 69.00/84.00 **st.**

XX Four Regions, 102-104 Kew Rd, TW9 2PQ, ℰ 940 9044, Chinese rest. – ▤
CX

Twickenham – ⊠ Middx. – ☎ 081.

🛚 Staines Rd ℰ 783 1698, W : 2 m. on A 305 – 🛚 Stawberry Hill, Wellesley
ℰ 894 1246 – 🖪 The Atrium, Civic Centre, York St. ℰ 891 7272.

XX **McClements,** 12 The Green, TW2 5AA, ℰ 755 0176 – ⌦. 🔼 🅰🅴 𝘝𝘐𝘚𝘈
BX
closed Saturday lunch, Sunday and 1 week Christmas – **M** 18.50/25.00 **t.** and a la ca
▯ 7.00.

XX **Lemachun,** 27 York St., TW1 3JZ, ℰ 892 7327, Chinese (Peking, Szechuan) rest. – ▤.
🅰🅴 ⓞ 𝘝𝘐𝘚𝘈
BX
closed Sunday – **M** 20.00/30.00 **t.** and a la carte.

XX Cézanne, 68 Richmond Rd, TW1 3BE, ℰ 892 3526 – 🔼 🅰🅴 ⓞ 𝘝𝘐𝘚𝘈
BX

SOUTHWARK Except where otherwise stated see pp. 10 and 11.

Bermondsey – ⊠ SE1 – ☎ 071.

X Blueprint Café, Design Museum, Butlers Wharf, Shad Thames St., SE1 2YD, ℰ 378 70
≤.
p. 27 PX

Dulwich – ⊠ SE19 – ☎ 081.

🛚 Dulwich, Sydenham Hill, Grange Lane, College Rd, ℰ 693 3961.

XX **Luigi's,** 129 Gipsy Hill, SE19 1QS, ℰ 670 1843, Italian rest. – ▤. 🔼 🅰🅴 ⓞ 𝘝𝘐𝘚𝘈
FX
closed Saturday lunch, Sunday and Bank Holidays – **M** a la carte 15.45/20.60 **t.** ▯ 4.90.

Rotherhithe – ⊠ SE16 – ☎ 071.

🏨 **Scandic Crown,** 265 Rotherhithe St., Nelson Dock, SE16 1EJ, ℰ 231 10
Fax 231 0599, ≤, 🛁, ☎, 🏊, ⌇ – ▮ ⌦ rm ▤ rest 📺 ☎ ⓑ 🅿 – 🔬 380. 🔼 🅰🅴 ⓞ
⌗
GV
M 16.00 **st.** and a la carte ▯ 8.00 – ⊆ 9.50 – **374 rm** 107.00/159.00 **st.**, **12 suites** 210.
275.00 **st.**

SUTTON pp. 8 and 9.

Sutton – ⊠ Surrey – ☎ 081.

🛚, 🛚 Oak Sports Centre, Woodmansterne Rd ℰ 643 8363, E : 1 ¼ m. on B 278.

🏨 **Holiday Inn,** Gibson Rd, SM1 2RF, ℰ 770 1311, Telex 911319, Fax 770 1539, 🛁, ☎, ⌇
▮ ⌦ rm ▤ rest 📺 ☎ 🅿 – 🔬 180. 🔼 🅰🅴 ⓞ 𝘝𝘐𝘚𝘈
EZ
M *(closed Saturday lunch)* 15.00/20.00 **st.** and a la carte ▯ 4.50 – ⊆ 9.50 – **115**
99.50/120.00 **st.**, **1 suite** 170.00/275.00 **st.** – SB (weekends only) 98.00 **st.**

🏨 **Thatched House,** 135-141 Cheam Rd, SM1 2BN, ℰ 642 3131, Fax 770 0684, ☞ – 📺
🅿. 🔼 𝘝𝘐𝘚𝘈
DZ
M *(closed Sunday dinner)* (lunch and Saturday dinner by arrangement)/dinner 19.50
▯ 3.95 – **27 rm** ⊆ 37.50/57.50 **st.**

XX Partners Brasserie, 23 Stonecot Hill, SM3 9HB, ℰ 644 7743 – ▤
DY

TOWER HAMLETS pp. 6 and 7.

Stepney – ⊠ E1 – ☎ 071.

XX Laksmi, 116 Mile End Rd, E1 4UN, ℰ 265 9403, Indian rest. – ▤
GV

Wapping – ⊠ E1 – ☎ 071.

XXX Quayside, International House, 1 St. Katherine's Way, E1 9UN, ℰ 481 097
▤
p. 27 PX

ANDSWORTH Except where otherwise stated see pp. 12 and 13.

Battersea – ⊠ SW8/SW11 – ☎ 071.

XX ❀ **L'Arlequin** (Delteil), 123 Queenstown Rd, SW8 3RH, ☎ 622 0555, Fax 498 0715, French rest. – ▤. ◪ ◭ ⑩ ▨ VISA DQ c
closed Saturday, Sunday and 3 weeks summer – **M** (booking essential) 20.50 st. (lunch) and a la carte 35.00/51.50 st. ₪ 6.00
Spec. Petit chou farci à l'ancienne, Gibier en saison, Soufflé chaud "Genevieve".

XX **Le Chausson,** Ransome's Dock, 35-37 Parkgate Rd, SW11 4NP, ☎ 223 1611, French rest. – ▤. ◪ ◭ ⑩ ▨ p. 25 HZ e
closed Saturday lunch, Sunday, last 3 weeks August and Christmas-New Year – **M** 17.00/ 25.00 t. and a la carte ₪ 4.50.

XX **Chada,** 208-210 Battersea Park Rd, SW11 4ND, ☎ 622 2209, Thai rest. – ▤. ◪ ◭ ⑩ ▨ VISA
closed Saturday lunch, Sunday and Bank Holidays – **M** a la carte 11.30/21.60 t. CQ x

XX **Lena's,** 196 Lavender Hill, SW11 1JA, ☎ 228 3735, Thai rest. – ▤. ◪ ◭ ⑩ ▨ VISA CQ z
closed Sunday lunch, Easter, 25 December and 1 January – **M** 15.00/25.00 st. and a la carte ₪ 4.95.

X **Brasserie Faubourg,** 28 Queenstown Rd, SW8 3RX, ☎ 622 6245 – ◪ VISA DQ n
closed lunch Monday and Saturday, Sunday, 26 August-3 September, 24-25 December and Bank Holidays – **M** 9.50/30.00 t. and a la carte ₪ 4.75.

Clapham – ⊠ SW11 – ☎ 071.

XX **Pollyanna's,** 2 Battersea Rise, SW11 1ED, ☎ 228 0316 – ◪ ◭ VISA CQ v
closed Sunday dinner, 24 to 27 December and 1 January – **M** (dinner only and Sunday lunch)/dinner 14.95/24.50 t. ₪ 5.95.

X **Jasmin,** 50 Battersea Rise, SW11 1EG, ☎ 228 0336, Chinese (Peking, Canton) rest. – ◪ ◭ ⑩ VISA – **M** 25.00 t. (lunch) and a la carte approx. 16.50 t. ₪ 4.00. CQ u

Putney – ⊠ SW15 – ☎ 081.

X **Le Cassis,** 30 Putney High St., SW15 1SQ, ☎ 788 8668, French rest. – ◪ ◭ ⑩ VISA
closed Saturday lunch and Sunday in summer – **M** (restricted lunch)/dinner a la carte 13.65/23.45 t. ₪ 4.30. AQ x

Tooting – ⊠ SW17 – ☎ 081.
CR c
X Oh Boy, 843 Garratt Lane, SW17 0PG, ☎ 947 9760, Thai rest. – ▤

Wandsworth – ⊠ SW12/SW17/SW18 – ☎ 081.

XXX ❀❀ **Harvey's** (White), 2 Bellevue Rd, SW17 7EG, ☎ 672 0114 – ▤. ◪ VISA CR e
closed Sunday, Monday, first 2 weeks August and 2 weeks Christmas – **M** (booking essential) 24.00/48.00 t. ₪ 10.00
Spec. Foie gras poché aux lentilles, Tête de porc braisée aux épices, Tarte Tatin aux poires.

X **Bombay Bicycle Club,** 95 Nightingale Lane, SW12, ☎ 673 6217, Indian rest. – ◪ VISA
closed Sunday and Bank Holidays – **M** (dinner only) 20.00 t. and a la carte ₪ 3.75. DR o

/ESTMINSTER (City of) .

Bayswater and Maida Vale – ⊠ W2/W9 – ☎ 071 – Except where otherwise stated see pp. 32 and 33.

🏨 **Royal Lancaster** (Rank), Lancaster Terr., W2 2TY, ☎ 262 6737, Telex 24822, Fax 724 3191, ≤ – ▯ ⇔ rm ▤ ▥ ☎ ❷ – 🔬 1 400. ◪ ◭ ⑩ VISA ❀ DZ e
M 20.50/23.00 t. and a la carte – 🖃 12.00 – **398 rm** 148.00/188.00 st., **20 suites** 395.00/ 850.00 st.

🏨 **Whites** (Mt. Charlotte Thistle), Bayswater Rd, 90-92 Lancaster Gate, W2 3NR, ☎ 262 2711, Telex 24771, Fax 262 2147 – ▯ ⇔ rm ▤ ▥ ☎. ◪ ◭ ⑩ VISA ❀
M (closed Saturday lunch) 16.00/21.50 t. and a la carte ₪ 7.15 – 🖃 10.00 – **52 rm** CZ v
135.00/225.00 st., **2 suites** 225.00/350.00 st. – SB 158.00/220.00 st.

🏨 **London Metropole,** Edgware Rd, W2 1JU, ☎ 402 4141, Telex 23711, Fax 724 8866, ≤, ⇔, ◻ – ▯ ⇔ rm ▤ ▥ ☎ – 🔬 1 250. ◪ ◭ ⑩ VISA ❀ p. 21 GU c
M 13.95/43.00 st. and a la carte ₪ 8.75 – 🖃 9.75 – **742 rm** 115.00/145.00 st., **24 suites** 150.00/550.00 st.

🏨 Plaza on Hyde Park (Hilton), Lancaster Gate, W2 3NA, ☎ 262 5022, Telex 8954372, Fax 724 8666 – ▯ ⇔ rm ▥ ☎ – 🔬 70 – **402 rm.** DZ x

🏨 Coburg, 129 Bayswater Rd, W2 4RJ, ☎ 221 2217, Telex 268235, Fax 229 0557 – ▯ ▥ ☎. ◪ ◭ ⑩ VISA. ❀ BZ c
M (see Spice Merchant below) – **131 rm** 🖃 79.50/129.50, **1 suite** 180.00.

🏨 Hyde Park Towers, 41-51 Inverness Terr., W2 3JN, ☎ 221 8484, Group Telex 263260, Fax 221 2286 – ▯ ▤ rest ▥ ☎ – 🔬 40 – **115 rm.** BZ r

🏨 Eden Park, 35-39 Inverness Terr., W2 3JS, ☎ 221 2220, Group Telex 263260, Fax 221 2286 – ⇔ rm ▤ rest ▥ ☎ – **137 rm.** BZ n

London Embassy (Jarvis), 150 Bayswater Rd., W2 4RT, ℰ 229 1212, Telex 2772? Fax 229 2623 – 🛊 ⇆ rm ■ 🔟 ☎ 🅿 – 🔬 60. 🛐 🖭 ⑨ 𝘝𝘐𝘚𝘈. ⅏
BZ
M (carving rest.) 19.00 **t.** and a la carte ⌀ 6.00 – ➗ 9.50 – **192 rm** 100.00/138.00 **t.**, **1 sui** 195.00 **t.** – SB (weekends only) 105.00/121.00 **st.**

Hospitality Inn (Mt. Charlotte Thistle), 104 Bayswater Rd., W2 3HL, ℰ 262 4461, Tel 22667, Fax 706 4560 – 🛊 ■ 🔟 📺 🅿 – 🔬 40. 🛐 🖭 ⑨ 𝘝𝘐𝘚𝘈
CZ
M (bar lunch)/dinner 13.25 **st.** and a la carte ⌀ 4.75 – ➗ 8.15 – **174 rm** 78.50/105.00 **s** **1 suite.**

Mornington (Best Western) without rest., 12 Lancaster Gate, W2 3LG, ℰ 262 7361, Tel 24281, Fax 706 1028, ☎ – 🛊 🔟 📺. 🛐 🖭 ⑨ 𝘝𝘐𝘚𝘈
DZ
closed 23 December-2 January – ➗ 5.00 – **68 rm** 75.00/103.00 **st.**

Pavilion, 35-39 Leinster Gdns., W2 3AR, ℰ 258 0269, Telex 268613, Fax 723 7295, ☎ – 🔟 📺 – 🔬 80. 🛐 🖭 ⑨ 𝘝𝘐𝘚𝘈. ⅏
DZ
M (dinner only) 15.00 **st.** and a la carte ⌀ 4.00 – ➗ 5.00 – **97 rm** 50.00/110.00 **st.** SB 80.00 **st.**

Byron without rest., 36-38 Queensborough Terr., W2 3SH, ℰ 243 0987, Telex 26343 Fax 792 1957 – 🛊 🔟 📺. 🛐 🖭 ⑨ 𝘝𝘐𝘚𝘈. ⅏
BZ
41 rm ➗ 70.00/95.00 **st.**, **1 suite** 135.00/150.00 **st.**

Century, 18-19 Craven Hill Gdns., W2 3EE, ℰ 262 6644, Telex 263813, Fax 262 0673 – 🛊 📺 ☎ – **60 rm.**
CZ

Delmere, 130 Sussex Gdns., W2 1UB, ℰ 706 3344, Telex 8953857, Fax 262 1863 – 🛊 📺. 🛐 🖭 ⑨ 𝘝𝘐𝘚𝘈
DZ
M (closed Sunday) (dinner only) 14.50 **t.** and a la carte ⌀ 3.75 – ➗ 6.00 – **38 rm** 71.4 87.00 **st.** – SB (weekends only) 72.00 **st.**

Camelot without rest., 45-47 Norfolk Sq., W2 1RX, ℰ 262 1980, Telex 2683? Fax 402 3412 – 🛊 📺 ☎. 🛐 𝘝𝘐𝘚𝘈 – ➗ 36.50/72.00 **st.**
DZ

Parkwood without rest., 4 Stanhope Pl., W2 2HB, ℰ 402 2241, Fax 402 1574 – ⇆ 📺 🛐 𝘝𝘐𝘚𝘈. ⅏ – **18 rm** ➗ 39.75/67.50 **st.**
EZ

Spice Merchant (at Coburg H.), 130 Bayswater Rd, W2 4RJ, ℰ 221 2442, Fax 229 055 Indian rest. – ■. 🛐 🖭 ⑨ 𝘝𝘐𝘚𝘈
BZ
M (buffet lunch)/dinner a la carte 9.00/15.00 **t.** ⌀ 5.50.

Poons, Whiteleys, Queensway, W21 4YN, ℰ 792 2884, Chinese rest. – ■. 🛐 🖭 ⑨ 𝘝 closed Christmas – **M** 5.00/10.00 **st.** and a la carte.
p. 32 BZ

San Marino, 26 Sussex Pl., W2 2TH, ℰ 723 8395, Italian rest. – 🛐 🖭 ⑨ 𝘝𝘐𝘚𝘈 closed Bank Holidays – **M** a la carte 17.20/22.50 **t.**
DZ

Hsing, 451 Edgware Rd, W2, ℰ 402 0904, Chinese rest. – 🛐 🖭 ⑨ 𝘝𝘐𝘚𝘈 closed Sunday – **M** a la carte 13.75/20.00 **t.**
GU

Al San Vincenzo, 30 Connaught Sq., W2 2AE, ℰ 262 9623, Italian rest. – 🛐 𝘝𝘐𝘚𝘈 EZ closed Saturday lunch, Sunday, 2 weeks August, Christmas and Bank Holidays – **M** 19.0 32.00 **t.** ⌀ 6.50.

Taxin Thai, 79 Castellain Rd, W9 1EU, ℰ 286 4801, Thai rest. – 🛐 🖭 ⑨ 𝘝𝘐𝘚𝘈 FT **M** (dinner only) 15.50 **t.** and a la carte.

Fortune Cookie, 1 Queensway, W2 4QJ, ℰ 727 7260, Chinese rest. – 🛐 𝘝𝘐𝘚𝘈 **M** 8.50 **t.** and a la carte.
BZ

Belgravia – ✉ SW1 – ✆ 071 – Except where otherwise stated see pp. 30 and 31.

Berkeley, Wilton Pl., SW1X 7RL, ℰ 235 6000, Telex 919252, Fax 235 4330, ⌀₅, ☎, 🛐 🛊 ■ 🔟 ☎ ⇆ – 🔬 200. 🛐 🖭 ⑨ 𝘝𝘐𝘚𝘈. ⅏
FQ
M Restaurant (closed Saturday) 19.50 **st.** (lunch) and a la carte 25.70/39.25 **st.** ⌀ 5.35 **Buttery** (closed Sunday) 15.00 **st.** (lunch) and a la carte 21.00/30.00 **st.** ⌀ 5.35 – ➗ 16.00 **132 rm** 170.00/275.00 **st.**, **27 suites** 440.00/495.00 **st.**

Sheraton Belgravia, 20 Chesham Pl., SW1X 8HQ, ℰ 235 6040, Telex 91902? Fax 259 6243 – 🛊 ⇆ rm ■ 🔟 ☎. 🛐 🖭 ⑨ 𝘝𝘐𝘚𝘈. ⅏
FR
M (closed lunch Saturday and Bank Holidays) 18.50/19.75 **t.** and a la carte ⌀ 5.00 – ➗ 11.7 – **82 rm** 230.00/250.00 **s.**, **7 suites** 310.00 **s.**

Halkin, 5 Halkin St., SW1X 7DJ, ℰ 333 1000, Telex 290308, Fax 333 1100 – 🛊 ■ 🔟 ☎ 🔬 25. 🛐 🖭 ⑨ 𝘝𝘐𝘚𝘈. ⅏
AV
M (Italian rest.) 22.50/35.00 **st.** and a la carte ⌀ 9.00 – ➗ 8.50 – **37 rm** 180.00/280.00 **s 4 suites** 300.00/450.00 **s.**

Lowndes, 21 Lowndes St., SW1X 9ES, ℰ 235 6020, Telex 919065, Fax 235 1154 – ⇆ rm ■ rest 🔟 ☎. 🛐 🖭 ⑨ 𝘝𝘐𝘚𝘈. ⅏
FR
M 15.50 **t.** (lunch) and a la carte 17.50/25.50 **st.** ⌀ 10.00 – ➗ 10.25 – **74 rm** 150.00 **s 5 suites** 300.00/450.00 **s..**

Diplomat without rest., 2 Chesham St., SW1X 8DT, ℰ 235 1544, Telex 92667 Fax 259 6153 – 🛊 🔟 ☎. 🛐 🖭 ⑨ 𝘝𝘐𝘚𝘈. ⅏
FR
27 rm ➗ 54.95/115.00 **s.**

Al Bustan, 27 Motcomb St., SW1X 8JU, ℰ 235 8277, Lebanese rest. – ■. 🛐 🖭 𝘝𝘐𝘚𝘈 closed 25 December and 1 January – **M** a la carte 20.25/26.75.
FR

Motcombs, 26 Motcomb St., SW1X 8JU, ℰ 235 6382, Fax 245 6351 – ■. 🛐 🖭 ⑨ 𝘝𝘐𝘚𝘈 closed Sunday and Bank Holidays – **M** 15.00 **t.** (lunch) and a la carte approx. 14.90 **t.** FR

Hyde Park and Knightsbridge – ⊠ SW1/SW7 – ❖ 071 – pp. 30 and 31.

🖪 Harrods, (Basement Banking Hall), Knightsbridge ✆ 730 3488/824 8844.

Hyde Park (Forte), 66 Knightsbridge, SW1Y 7LA, ✆ 235 2000, Telex 262057, Fax 235 4552, ← – ▯ ❄ rm ▯ ☎ க் – ▵ 230. ◪ ▣ ▥ ▥ EQ **v**
M Park Room 24.50/35.00 **st.** ▯ 10.00 – Grill Room *(closed Saturday and Sunday)* 34.50/ 48.50 **st.** ▯ 10.00 – ☑ 14.00 – **166 rm** 199.00/285.00 **st.**, **19 suites** 525.00/1 400.00 **st.**

Knightsbridge Green without rest., 159 Knightsbridge, SW1X 7PD, ✆ 584 6274, Fax 225 1635 – ▯ ▥ ▥ ▥ ▥ EQ **z**
closed Christmas – ☑ 8.50 – **10 rm** 85.00/100.00 **st.**, **14 suites** 115.00 **st.**

X **Lucullus**, 48 Knightsbridge, SW1X 7JN, ✆ 245 6622, Fax 245 6625, Seafood – ▤ FQ **a**
M 12.50 **t.** (lunch) and dinner a la carte approx. 33.00 **t.** ▯ 5.00.

X **Dell Arte**, 116 Knightsbridge, SW1X 7PJ, ✆ 225 3512, Italian rest. – ◪ ▣ ▥ ▥ EQ **x**
closed Sunday – M 12.50/26.00 **t.** and a la carte ▯ 4.00.

Mayfair – ⊠ W1 – ❖ 071 – pp. 28 and 29.

Claridge's, Brook St., W1A 2JQ, ✆ 629 8860, Telex 21872, Fax 499 2210 – ▯ ▤ ▥ ☎ க்.
◪ ▣ ▥ ▥ ▥ BL **c**
M 48.00/58.00 **st.** and a la carte 34.50/63.50 **st.** ▯ 5.80 – Causerie *(closed Saturday)* 18.50/ 30.00 **st.** and a la carte 29.50/47.50 **st.** ▯ 5.80 – ☑ 15.75 – **137 rm** 190.00/290.00 **st.**, **53 suites** 490.00/1 125.00 **st.**

Dorchester, Park Lane, W1A 2HJ, ✆ 629 8888, Telex 887704, Fax 409 0114, ƒ₅, ≘s – ▯
⇔ rm ▤ ▥ ☎ க் ⇔ – ▵ 500. ◪ ▣ ▥ ▥ ▥ BN **a**
M Terrace *(closed Sunday, Monday and 26 December)* (dinner only) 35.00 **st.** and a la carte 32.50/48.50 **st.** ▯ 9.00 – Grill 25.00/45.00 **st.** and a la carte 22.00/31.00 **st.** ▯ 9.00 (see also Oriental below) – ☑ 12.50 – **202 rm** 180.00/240.00 **s.**, **50 suites** 380.00/1 000.00 **s.**

Four Seasons Inn on the Park, Hamilton Pl., Park Lane, W1A 1AZ, ✆ 499 0888, Telex 22771, Fax 493 1895 – ▯ ⇔ rm ▤ ▥ ☎ க் ⇔ – ▵ 400. ◪ ▣ ▥ ▥ BP **a**
M Lanes 26.10/30.80 **st.** and dinner a la carte 30.80/36.85 **st.** ▯ 7.45 – (see also Four Seasons below) – ☑ 7.45 – **209 rm** 209.00/260.00 **s.**, **19 suites** 308.00/1 045.00 **s.**

Le Meridien London, 21 Piccadilly, W1V 0BH, ✆ 734 8000, Telex 25795, Fax 437 3574, ƒ₅, ≘s, ⃞, squash – ▯ ▤ ▥ ☎ க் – ▵ 200. ◪ ▣ ▥ ▥ ▥ EM **a**
M Terrace Garden 19.00 **t.** (lunch) and a la carte 15.70/24.35 **t.** ▯ 8.20 – (see also Oak Room below) – ☑ 11.50 – **210 rm** 190.00/230.00. **50 suites** 300.00/550.00.

Grosvenor House (Forte), Park Lane, W1A 3AA, ✆ 499 6363, Telex 24871, Fax 493 3341, ƒ₅, ≘s, ⃞ – ▯ ⇔ rm ▤ ▥ ☎ க் – ▵ 1 000. ◪ ▣ ▥ ▥ ▥ AM **a**
M 15.50/19.50 **st.** and a la carte – (see also 90 Park Lane below) – ☑ 11.75 – **384 rm** 160.00/210.00 **st.**, **163 suites** 285.00/690.00 **st.** – SB (weekends only) 198.00 **st.**

❖ **Connaught**, Carlos Pl., W1Y 6AL, ✆ 499 7070, Fax 495 3262 – ▯ ▤ rest ▥ ☎. ◪ ▥
▥ BM **e**
M (booking essential) 22.80/55.80 **t.** and a la carte 28.10/59.00 **t.** ▯ 5.00 – **66 rm 24 suites**
Spec. Galette Connaught aux diamants noirs, Salade Aphrodite, Homard et langoustines grillés aux herbes, Crème brûlée d'un soir.

Le Gavroche at Fortyseven Park, 47 Park St., W1Y 4EB, ✆ 491 7282, Telex 22116, Fax 491 7281 – ▯ ▤ ▥ ☎ – ▵ 30. ◪ ▣ ▥ ▥ ▥ AM **c**
M (see Le Gavroche below) – ☑ 15.50 – **52 suites** 225.00/430.00 **s.**

Britannia (Inter-Con.), Grosvenor Sq., W1A 3AN, ✆ 629 9400, Telex 23941, Fax 629 7736
– ▯ ⇔ rm ▤ ▥ ☎ – ▵ 80. ◪ ▣ ▥ ▥ ▥ BM **x**
M 21.30 **st.** and a la carte ▯ 12.00 – (see also Shogun below) – ☑ 10.75 – **314 rm** 175.00/210.00. **12 suites** 375.00/500.00.

Park Lane, Piccadilly, W1Y 8BX, ✆ 499 6321, Telex 21533, Fax 499 1965, ƒ₅ – ▯ ⇔ rm
▥ ☎ ⓟ – ▵ 500. ◪ ▣ ▥ ▥ ▥ BP **x**
M *(closed Sunday and Bank Holidays)* 16.00/22.00 **st.** and a la carte ▯ 10.00 – ☑ 10.75 –
266 rm 147.00/175.00 **s.**, **54 suites** 205.00 **s.**

London Hilton on Park Lane, 22 Park Lane, W1Y 2HH, ✆ 493 8000, Telex 24873, Fax 493 4957, « ← London from Window on the World restaurant », ≘s – ▯ ⇔ rm ▤ ▥
☎ க் – ▵ 1 000. ◪ ▣ ▥ ▥ ▥ BP **e**
M 36.00/55.00 **t.** and a la carte ▯ 14.00 – ☑ 13.95 – **396 rm. 52 suites.**

Inter-Continental, 1 Hamilton Pl., Hyde Park Corner, W1V 0QY, ✆ 409 3131, Telex 25853, Fax 409 7460, ƒ₅, ≘s – ▯ ⇔ rm ▤ ▥ ☎ க் ⇔ – ▵ 700. ◪ ▣ ▥ ▥ ▥
M 20.50 **t.** and a la carte ▯ 7.50 (see also Le Soufflé below) – ☑ 14.95 – **438 rm** 190.00/ 250.00 **s.**, **3 suites** 270.00/1 200.00 **s.** BP **o**

May Fair Inter-Continental, Stratton St., W1A 2AN, ✆ 629 7777, Telex 262526, Fax 629 1459, ƒ₅, ≘s, ⃞ – ▯ ▤ ⇔ rm ▤ ▥ ☎ க் – ▵ 270. ◪ ▣ ▥ ▥ ▥ DN **z**
M (see Le Chateau below) – ☑ 10.50 – **269 rm** 140.00/235.00. **24 suites** 400.00/1 400.00 – SB (weekends only) 238.00/250.00 **st.**

Brown's (Forte), 29-34 Albemarle St., W1A 4SW, ✆ 493 6020, Fax 493 9381 – ▯ ⇔ rm
▤ rest ▥ ☎ – ▵ 80. ◪ ▣ ▥ ▥ ▥ DM **e**
M 23.00 **st.** and a la carte ▯ 7.00 – ☑ 10.75 – **127 rm** 160.00/198.00 **st.**, **6 suites** 330.00/ 400.00 **st.** – SB (weekends only) 198.00 **st.**

Marriott, Duke St., Grosvenor Sq., W1A 4AW, ℰ 493 1232, Telex 268101, Fax 491 320
🛗 😝 🔟 ☎ � – ⚫ 375. 🄰 🄰🄴 ⓞ 𝑉𝐼𝑆𝐴. ⚫
BL
M *(closed Saturday lunch)* 25.00 **t.** (lunch) and a la carte 21.75/28.45 **t.** – ☲ 9.75 – **206**
100.00/230.00 **s.. 17 suites** 290.00 **s.**

Atheneaum (Rank), 116 Piccadilly, W1V 0BJ, ℰ 499 3464, Telex 261589, Fax 493 186
😝 😝 rm 🗏 🔟 ☎ – ⚫ 55. 🄰 🄰🄴 ⓞ 𝑉𝐼𝑆𝐴. ⚫
CF
M *(closed Saturday lunch)* 22.50 **st.** and a la carte ⏐ 8.15 – ☲ 12.85 – **90 rm** 178.
213.00 **st.. 22 suites** 330.00 **st.**

Westbury (Forte), Conduit St., W1A 4UH, ℰ 629 7755, Telex 24378, Fax 495 1163 –
😝 rm 🗏 🔟 ☎ – ⚫ 110. 🄰 🄰🄴 ⓞ 𝑉𝐼𝑆𝐴
DM
M 15.00/22.00 **st.** and a la carte ⏐ 7.45 – ☲ 11.50 – **229 rm** 155.00/180.00 **st., 14 sui**
255.00/555.00 **st.** – SB (weekends only) 138.00 **st.**

Holiday Inn, 3 Berkeley St., W1X 6NE, ℰ 493 8282, Telex 24561, Fax 629 2827 –
😝 rm 🗏 🔟 ☎ – ⚫ 70. 🄰 🄰🄴 ⓞ 𝑉𝐼𝑆𝐴 ⚫
DN
M (bar lunch Saturday) 17.00/23.00 **t.** and a la carte ⏐ 8.95 – ☲ 11.75 – **178 rm** 164.
220.00 **st.. 7 suites** 330.00/600.00 **st.**

Washington, Curzon St., W1 8DT, ℰ 499 7000, Telex 24540, Fax 495 6172 – 🛗 😝 rm
🔟 ☎ – ⚫ 80. 🄰 🄰🄴 ⓞ 𝑉𝐼𝑆𝐴. ⚫
CN
M 20.00 25.00 **st.** ⏐ 7.00 – ☲ 10.50 – **169 rm** 141.00/172.00 **st.. 4 suites** 230.00/385.00

Chesterfield, 35 Charles St., W1X 8LX, ℰ 491 2622, Telex 269394, Fax 491 4793 –
😝 rm 🔟 ☎ – ⚫ 100. 🄰 🄰🄴 ⓞ 𝑉𝐼𝑆𝐴. ⚫
CN
M 22.50/24.00 **t.** and a la carte ⏐ 6.00 – ☲ 9.95 – **109 rm** 115.00/170.00 **st.. 4 suit**
150.00/300.00 **st.**

Green Park, Half Moon St., W1Y 8BP, ℰ 629 7522, Telex 28856, Fax 491 8971 – 🛗 😝
🗏 rest 🔟 ☎ – ⚫ 70. 🄰 🄰🄴 ⓞ 𝑉𝐼𝑆𝐴. ⚫
CN
M 16.50 **st.** and a la carte ⏐ 5.10 – ☲ 9.75 – **161 rm** 104.00/174.00 **st.**

Flemings, 7-12 Half Moon St., W1Y 7RA, ℰ 499 2964, Telex 27510, Fax 499 1817 –
🗏 rest 🔟 ☎ – ⚫ 45. 🄰 🄰🄴 ⓞ 𝑉𝐼𝑆𝐴 ⚫
CN
M 15.50 **st.** and a la carte ⏐ 5.75 – ☲ 10.20 – **132 rm** 97.00/184.00 **st.. 11 suites** 184.
230.00 **st.** – SB 130.00 **st.**

London Mews Hilton without rest., 2 Stanhope Row, W1Y 7HE, ℰ 493 7222, Te
24665, Fax 629 9423 – 🛗 😝 🗏 🔟 ☎ 🚗 – ⚫ 50. 🄰 🄰🄴 ⓞ 𝑉𝐼𝑆𝐴. ⚫
BP
71 rm ☲ 146.00/174.00 **st.. 1 suite** 350.00 **st.**

XXXXX ✿ **Oak Room** (at Le Meridien London H.), 21 Piccadilly, W1V OBH, ℰ 734 8000, Te
25795, Fax 437 3574, French rest. – 🗏. 🄰 🄰🄴 ⓞ 𝑉𝐼𝑆𝐴
EM
closed Saturday lunch and Sunday – **M** 23.00/44.00 **t.** and a la carte 30.00/40.00 **t.** ⏐ 9.
Spec. Gazpacho de langoustines à la crème de courgette, Suprême de bar au beurre de truffe, Canard, sauce Arab

XXXXX **90 Park Lane** (at Grosvenor House H.), Park Lane, W1A 3AA, ℰ 409 1290, Fax 493 334
🗏. 🄰 🄰🄴 ⓞ 𝑉𝐼𝑆𝐴
AM
M 15.50/19.50 **st.** and a la carte ⏐ 14.50.

XXXX ✿✿✿ **Le Gavroche** (Roux), 43 Upper Brook St., W1Y 1PF, ℰ 408 0881, Fax 409 093
French rest. – 🗏. 🄰 🄰🄴 ⓞ 𝑉𝐼𝑆𝐴
AM
closed Saturday, Sunday, 21 December-2 January and Bank Holidays – **M** (booki
essential) 30.00/60.00 **st.** and a la carte 41.50/76.10 **st.** ⏐ 13.00
Spec. Soufflé suissesse, Tournedos gratiné aux poivres, Sablé aux fraises.

XXXX **Oriental** (at Dorchester H.), Park Lane, W1A 2HJ, ℰ 629 8888, Telex 8877(
Fax 409 0114, Chinese (Canton) rest. – 🗏. 🄰 🄰🄴 ⓞ 𝑉𝐼𝑆𝐴
BN
closed Saturday lunch, Sunday, 25 December and 1 January – **M** 20.00/30.00 **st.** and a
carte 23.00/31.00 **st.** ⏐ 9.00.

XXXX ✿ **Four Seasons** (at Inn on the Park H.), Hamilton Pl., Park Lane, W1A 1AZ, ℰ 499 088
Telex 22771, Fax 493 1895, French rest. – 🗏 🚗. 🄰 🄰🄴 ⓞ 𝑉𝐼𝑆𝐴
BP
M 24.75/44.00 **st.** and a la carte 33.80/53.10 **st.** ⏐ 7.45
Spec. Delices du Sud-Ouest, Baron de lapereau, étuvée de carottes au gingembre, Parfait glacé à l'orange et à
cardamume, sauce chocolat.

XXXX **Le Soufflé** (at Inter-Continental H.), 1 Hamilton Pl., Hyde Park Corner, W1V 0Q
ℰ 409 3131, Telex 25853, Fax 409 7460 – 🗏 🚗. 🄰 🄰🄴 ⓞ 𝑉𝐼𝑆𝐴
BP
closed Saturday lunch – **M** 25.50/40.00 **t.** and a la carte 33.20/58.20 **t.** ⏐ 9.00.

XXXX **Le Chateau** (at May Fair Inter-Continental H.), Stratton Pl., W1A 2AN, ℰ 629 7777, Tele
262526, Fax 629 1459, French rest. – 🗏. 🄰 🄰🄴 ⓞ 𝑉𝐼𝑆𝐴
DN
closed Saturday lunch – **M** 20.00/32.50 **t.** and a la carte.

XXX **Princess Garden,** 8-10 North Audley St., W1Y 1WF, ℰ 493 3223, Fax 491 2655, Chines
(Peking) rest. – 🗏. 🄰 🄰🄴 ⓞ 𝑉𝐼𝑆𝐴
AL
closed 1 week Christmas – **M** 20.00/35.00 **t.** and a la carte ⏐ 8.00.

XXX **Empress Garden,** 15-16 Berkeley St., W1X 5AE, ℰ 493 1381, Chinese (Peking, Canto
rest. – 🗏. 🄰 🄰🄴 ⓞ 𝑉𝐼𝑆𝐴
DN
closed 25 and 26 December – **M** 20.00/70.00 **t.** and a la carte ⏐ 7.50.

XXX **Zen Central,** 20-22 Queen St., W1X 7PJ, ℰ 629 8089, Chinese rest. – 🗏 🄿. 🄰 🄰🄴 ⓞ
𝑉𝐼𝑆𝐴
CN
M a la carte approx. 18.50 **t.** ⏐ 6.00.

XX **Greenhouse,** 27a Hay's Mews, W1X 7RJ, ℰ 499 3331 – 🝙, 🝙 🝙 🝙 🝙 🝙 BN **a**
closed Saturday lunch, Sunday dinner and 24 December-2 January – **M** a la carte 19.50/
26.00. 🝙 5.00.

XX **Copper Chimney,** 13 Heddon St., W1R 7LF, ℰ 439 2004, Indian rest. – 🝙, 🝙 🝙 🝙 🝙
🝙🝙🝙 EM **e**
closed 25 December and 1 January – **M** 18.50 **t.** (dinner) and a la carte 19.00/25.00.

XX **Ho-Ho,** 29 Maddox St., W1R 9LD, ℰ 493 1228, Oriental cuisine – 🝙, 🝙 🝙 🝙
DL **x**
closed Sunday and Bank Holidays – **M** 17.80/23.00 **t.** and a la carte.

XX **Langan's Brasserie,** Stratton St., W1X 5FD, ℰ 491 8822 – 🝙 DN **e**

XX **Shogun** (at Britannia H.) Adams Row, W1Y 5DE, ℰ 493 1255, Japanese rest. – 🝙, 🝙 🝙
🝙 🝙🝙🝙 BM **x**
closed Monday and Christmas-New Year – **M** (dinner only) 30.50 **t.** and a la carte 🝙 5.00.

XX **Miyama,** 38 Clarges St., W1Y 7PJ, ℰ 499 2443, Japanese rest. – 🝙, 🝙 🝙
CN **e**
🝙🝙🝙
closed Saturday lunch, Sunday and Bank Holidays – **M** 15.00/32.00 **t.** and a la carte 🝙 7.00.

XX **La Seppia,** 8a Mount St., W1, ℰ 499 3385, Italian Seafood rest. – 🝙, 🝙 🝙 🝙 🝙 🝙
closed Saturday, Sunday. last 3 weeks August, 10 days at Christmas and Bank Holidays –
M 20.50 **t.** and a la carte 🝙 5.50. BM **v**

X **Ikeda,** 30 Brook St., W1Y 1AG, ℰ 629 2730, Japanese rest. – 🝙 CKL **a**

Regent's Park and Marylebone – ✉ NW1/NW6/NW8/W1 – ☏ 071 – Except where
otherwise stated see pp. 28 and 29.

🛈 Basement Services Arcade, Selfridges Store, Oxford St., W1 ℰ 730 3488.

🏨🏨🏨🏨 **Churchill,** 30 Portman Sq., W1A 4ZX, ℰ 486 5800, Telex 264831, Fax 935 0431, 🝙 – 🝙
🝙 rm 🝙 🝙 🝙 – 🝙 200. 🝙 🝙 🝙 🝙 🝙. 🝙 AJ **x**
M 29.00 **t.** (lunch) and a la carte 22.75/36.70 **t.** 🝙 4.50 – 🖵 15.00 – **403 rm** 185.00/200.00 **s.,**
49 suites 300.00/995.00 **s.**

🏨🏨🏨🏨 **Portman Inter-Continental,** 22 Portman Sq., W1H 9FL, ℰ 486 5844, Telex 261526,
Fax 935 0537, 🝙 – 🝙 🝙 🝙 rm 🝙 🝙 🝙 🝙 🝙 – 🝙 380. 🝙 🝙 🝙 🝙. 🝙 AJ **o**
M 19.50/26.50 **st.** and a la carte 🝙 10.50 – 🖵 12.50 – **262 rm** 153.00/185.00 **t., 10 suites**
400.00/700.00 **t.**

🏨🏨🏨🏨 **Langham Hilton,** 1 Portland Place, W1N 3AA, ℰ 636 1000, Telex 21113, Fax 323 2340 –
🝙 🝙 rm 🝙 🝙 🝙 🝙 – 🝙 360. 🝙 🝙 🝙 🝙 p. 21 JU **e**
M 22.00/29.50 **t.** and a la carte 🝙 7.00 – 🖵 15.50 – **365 rm** 170.00/255.00 **s., 20 suites**
380.00/1 100.00 **s.**

🏨🏨🏨 **Selfridge** (Mt. Charlotte Thistle), 400 Orchard St., W1H 0JS, ℰ 408 2080, Telex 22361,
Fax 629 8849 – 🝙 🝙 rm 🝙 🝙 🝙 – 🝙 220. 🝙 🝙 🝙 🝙. 🝙 AK **e**
M *(closed Saturday lunch and Sunday)* 19.75 **st.** and a la carte 🝙 5.25 – 🖵 10.20 – **294 rm**
135.00/160.00 **st., 2 suites** 350.00 **st.**

🏨🏨🏨 **Berkshire** (Edwardian), 350 Oxford St., W1N 0BY, ℰ 629 7474, Telex 22270,
Fax 629 8156 – 🝙 🝙 rm 🝙 🝙 🝙 – 🝙 40. 🝙 🝙 🝙 🝙. 🝙 BK **n**
M *(closed Saturday lunch)* 28.00/35.00 **st.** and a la carte 🝙 6.00 – 🖵 13.50 – **145 rm**
158.00/245.00 **st., 2 suites** 300.00/450.00 **st.**

🏨🏨🏨 **Clifton Ford,** 47 Welbeck St., W1M 8DN, ℰ 486 6600, Telex 22569, Fax 486 7492 – 🝙
🝙 rm 🝙 🝙 🝙 – 🝙 80. 🝙 🝙 🝙 🝙 BH **a**
M 21.50/29.00 **st.** and a la carte 🝙 5.00 – 🖵 12.95 – **196 rm** 120.00/135.00 **s., 4 suites**
300.00 **s.**

🏨🏨🏨 **Ramada H. London,** 10 Berners St., W1A 3BE, ℰ 636 1629, Telex 25759, Fax 580 3972 –
🝙 🝙 rm 🝙 rest 🝙 🝙 🝙 – 🝙 120. 🝙 🝙 🝙 🝙. 🝙 EJ **r**
M *(closed Saturday lunch)* 13.50/15.75 **st.** and a la carte 🝙 5.00 – 🖵 9.75 – **232 rm** 100.00/
150.00 **st., 3 suites** 300.00/450.00 **st.** – SB (weekends only) 150.00/198.00 **st.**

🏨🏨🏨 **London Regent's Park Hilton,** 18 Lodge Rd, NW8 7JT, ℰ 722 7722, Telex 23101,
Fax 483 2408 – 🝙 🝙 🝙 🝙 🝙 🝙 – 🝙 150. 🝙 🝙 🝙 🝙. 🝙 p. 21 GT **v**
M *(closed Saturday lunch)* (carving rest.) 20.00/30.00 **t.** and a la carte 🝙 7.25 – 🖵 11.30 –
376 rm 119.50/159.50 **st., 1 suite** 191.00/251.00 **st.**

🏨🏨🏨 **Montcalm,** Great Cumberland Pl., W1A 2LF, ℰ 402 4288, Telex 28710, Fax 724 9180 – 🝙
🝙 rm 🝙 🝙 – 🝙 60. 🝙 🝙 🝙 🝙. 🝙 p. 33 EZ **x**
M *(closed lunch Saturday. Sunday and Bank Holidays)* 17.75/21.95 **t.** and a la carte 🝙 6.00 –
🖵 12.00 – **101 rm** 167.00/215.00 **st., 14 suites** 270.00/600.00 **st.**

🏨🏨🏨 **St. George's** (Forte), Langham Pl., W1N 8QS, ℰ 580 0111, Fax 436 7997, ← – 🝙 🝙 rm
🝙 rest 🝙 🝙 – 🝙 35. 🝙 🝙 🝙 🝙 p. 21 JU **a**
M *(closed lunch Saturday and Sunday)* 15.50 **st.** and a la carte 🝙 7.00 – 🖵 10.95 – **83 rm**
95.00/120.00 **st., 3 suites** 200.00 **st.** – SB (weekends only) 118.00 **st.**

🏨🏨🏨 **Holiday Inn,** 134 George St., W1H 6DN, ℰ 723 1277, Telex 27983, Fax 402 0666, 🝙, 🝙,
🝙 – 🝙 🝙 rm 🝙 🝙 🝙 🝙 🝙 – 🝙 120. 🝙 🝙 🝙 🝙. 🝙 p. 33 EZ **i**
M 15.00/25.00 **st.** and a la carte 🝙 7.40 – 🖵 11.25 – **239 rm** 152.00/180.00 **st., 2 suites**
495.00/595.00 **st.**

Forte Crest, Carburton St., W1P 8EE, ℰ 388 2300, Fax 387 2806 – 🛗 ⇌ rm 🔳 rest 📺 ℗ – 🔬 500. 🔼 🌃 ⓞ 𝘝𝘐𝘚𝘈
p. 21 JU
M 7.50/14.50 **st.** and a la carte ⫲ 5.00 – ⊡ 8.25 – **312 rm** 95.00/105.00 **st.**, **5 suites** 150.0
175.00 **st.** – SB (weekends only) 98.00 **st.**

Dorset Square, 39-40 Dorset Sq., NW1 6QN, ℰ 723 7874, Telex 263964, Fax 724 332
« Attractively furnished Regency town houses » – 🛗 🔳 📺 ☎. 🔼 🌃 𝘝𝘐𝘚𝘈 ✳
M (closed Sunday lunch and Saturday) 27.00 **t.** ⫲ 14.95 – ⊡ 9.50 – **37 rm** 90.00/165.00
p. 21 HU

Durrants, 26-32 George St., W1H 6BJ, ℰ 935 8131, Telex 894919, Fax 487 3510, « Converted Georgian houses with Regency façade » – 🛗 🔳 📺 ☎ – 🔬 40. 🔼 🌃 𝘝𝘐𝘚𝘈 ✳
M 25.00/35.00 **st.** and a la carte ⫲ 4.50 – ⊡ 8.25 – **93 rm** 58.00/135.00 **st.**, **3 suite**
136.00/185.00 **st.**
AH

Londoner, 57-59 Welbeck St., W1M 8HS, ℰ 935 4442, Telex 894630, Fax 487 3782 –
⇌ rm 📺 ☎ – 🔬 90
BJ
144 rm.

Rathbone, Rathbone St., W1P 1AJ, ℰ 636 2001, Telex 28728, Fax 636 3882 – 🛗 ⇌ r
🔳 📺 ☎. 🔼 🌃 ⓞ 𝘝𝘐𝘚𝘈 ✳
p. 22 KU
M (closed Sunday lunch, Saturday and Bank Holidays) 12.50/15.50 **st.** and a la carte ⫲ 5.6
– ⊡ 9.50 – **68 rm** 95.00/140.00 **st.**, **4 suites** 150.00/185.00 **st.**

Langham Court, 31-35 Langham St., W1N 5RE, ℰ 436 6622, Telex 21331, Fax 436 2303
🛗 📺 ☎ – 🔬 50
JU
56 rm.

Mostyn, 4 Bryanston St., W1H 0DE, ℰ 935 2361, Fax 487 2759 – 🛗 📺 ☎ – 🔬 150. 🔼 🌃
ⓞ 𝘝𝘐𝘚𝘈 ✳
AK
M 25.00 **st.** (lunch) and a la carte 16.00/22.50 **st.** ⫲ 5.00 – ⊡ 8.75 – **118 rm** 92.00/124.00 **s**
3 suites 160.00/200.00 **st.**

Savoy Court (Edwardian), 13-25 Granville Pl., W1H 0EH, ℰ 408 0130, Telex 895551
Fax 493 2070 – 🛗 📺 ☎. 🔼 🌃 ⓞ 𝘝𝘐𝘚𝘈 ✳
AK
M (closed Saturday lunch and Sunday) 12.50/14.50 **st.** and a la carte ⫲ 6.50 – ⊡ 9.15
97 rm 81.00/118.00 **st.**

Harewood (Best Western), Harewood Row, NW1 6SE, ℰ 262 2707, Telex 29722
Fax 262 2975 – 🛗 ⇌ rm 🔳 rest 📺 ☎ – 🔬 100. ✳
p. 21 HU
93 rm.

Bryanston Court (Best Western) without rest., 56-60 Great Cumberland Pl., W1H 7FI
ℰ 262 3141, Group Telex 262076, Fax 262 7248 – 🛗 📺 ☎. 🔼 🌃 ⓞ 𝘝𝘐𝘚𝘈
⊡ 6.00 – **54 rm** 70.00/85.00 **st.**
p. 33 EZ

Blandford without rest., 80 Chiltern St., W1M 1PS, ℰ 486 3103, Telex 26259
Fax 487 2786 – 🛗 📺 ☎. 🔼 🌃 ⓞ 𝘝𝘐𝘚𝘈 ✳
p. 21 HU
33 rm ⊡ 63.00/98.00 **st.**

Concorde without rest., 50 Great Cumberland Pl., W1H 7FD, ℰ 402 6169, Group Tele
262076, Fax 262 7248 – 🛗 📺 ☎. 🔼 🌃 ⓞ 𝘝𝘐𝘚𝘈 ✳
p. 33 EZ
closed 28 December-3 January – ⊡ 8.00 – **28 rm** 65.00/75.00 **st.**

XXXX ✿✿ **Chez Nico** (Ladenis), 35 Great Portland St., W1N 5DD, ℰ 436 8846, French rest.
🔳. 🔼 ⓞ 𝘝𝘐𝘚𝘈
DJ
closed Bank Holiday lunch, Saturday, Sunday, Easter and 10 days at Christmas – ▯
(booking essential) 27.75/60.00 **st.**
Spec. Grillade de St. Jacques, Loup de mer au fenouil, Rouget au parfum de romarin purée au basilic.

XXX **Rue St. Jacques**, 5 Charlotte St., W1P 1HD, ℰ 637 0222, French rest. – 🔳. 🔼 🌃 ⓞ 𝘝𝘐
closed Saturday lunch, Sunday, Easter, Christmas-New Year and Bank Holidays – **M** 25.00
38.00 **t.** ⫲ 6.25.
p. 22 KU

XXX **Martin's**, 239 Baker St., NW1 6XE, ℰ 935 3130 – 🔳. 🔼 🌃 ⓞ 𝘝𝘐𝘚𝘈
p. 21 HU
closed Saturday, Sunday, Christmas and Bank Holidays – **M** a la carte 27.00/44.50 **t.** ⫲ 6.7

XXX **Odins**, 27 Devonshire St., W1N 1RJ, ℰ 935 7296
p. 21 IU

XX **Masako**, 6-8 St. Christopher's Pl., W1M 5HB, ℰ 935 1579, Japanese rest.
BJ
closed Sunday, 4 May, 31 August, Christmas and New Year – **M** 35.00/60.00 **t.** and a
carte.

XX **Gaylord**, 79-81 Mortimer St., W1N 7TB, ℰ 580 3615, Indian and Pakistani rest. – 🔳. 🔼
🌃 ⓞ 𝘝𝘐𝘚𝘈
p. 22 KU
M 11.50/15.00 **t.** and a la carte ⫲ 3.50.

XX **Maroush III**, 62 Seymour St., W1H 5AF, ℰ 724 5024, Lebanese rest. – 🔳   p. 33 EZ

XX **Stephen Bull**, 5-7 Blandford St., W1H 3AA, ℰ 486 9696 – 🔼 𝘝𝘐𝘚𝘈
AH
closed Saturday lunch, Sunday and 23 December-2 January – **M** a la carte approx. 22.50
⫲ 5.00.

XX **Mon**, (at Cumberland H.), Marble Arch, W1A 4RF, ℰ 262 6528, Japanese rest.
🔳
AK

XX **The Restaurant**, Jason Court, 76 Wigmore St., W1H 9DQ, ℰ 224 2992 – 🔳. 🔼
𝘝𝘐𝘚𝘈
BJ
closed Saturday lunch, Sunday, 1 week August, 2 weeks Christmas-New Year and Bank
Holidays – **M** 16.00/18.00 **t.** and a la carte ⫲ 4.50.

X **Asuka,** Berkeley Arcade, 209a Baker St., NW1 6AB, ℰ 486 5026, Fax 262 1456, Japanese rest. – 🔼 🕮 ⓪ 𝘝𝘐𝘚𝘈   p. 21 HU **u**
closed Saturday lunch, Sunday and Bank Holidays – **M** 15.50/55.00 **st.** and a la carte � 6.00.

X **Le P'tit Montmartre,** 15-17 Marylebone Lane, W1M 5FE, ℰ 935 9226, French rest. – ▤. 🔼 🕮 ⓪ 𝘝𝘐𝘚𝘈   BJ **a**
closed Saturday lunch, Sunday, Easter, 4 days at Christmas and Bank Holidays – **M** 16.95 **t.** and a la carte ⓛ 4.50.

X **Fontana Amorosa,** 1 Blenheim Terr., NW8 0EH, ℰ 328 5014, Italian rest. – 🔼 🕮 ⓪ 𝘝𝘐𝘚𝘈
closed Monday lunch, Sunday, mid August-mid September and Bank Holidays – **M** a la carte 17.90/27.20 **t.**   p. 20 FS **s**

X **Tino's,** 128 Allitsen Rd, NW8 7AU, ℰ 586 6264 – 🔼 🕮 𝘝𝘐𝘚𝘈   p. 21 GT **u**
closed 17 April, 25 December and 1 January – **M** 13.50 **t.** (lunch) and a la carte 15.30/21.35 **t.** ⓛ 4.95.

X **La Loggia,** 68 Edgware Rd, W2 2EG, ℰ 723 0554, Italian rest. – ▤. 🔼 🕮 ⓪ 𝘝𝘐𝘚𝘈
closed Saturday lunch, Sunday and Bank Holidays – **M** a la carte 18.00/27.70 **t.** ⓛ 4.00.
                                                 p. 33 EZ **a**

X **Au Bois St. Jean,** 122 St. John's Wood High St., NW8 7SG, ℰ 722 0400, French rest. – 🔼 🕮 𝘝𝘐𝘚𝘈   p. 21 GT **e**
closed 25 and 26 December – **M** 28.00 **t.** (dinner) and a la carte 13.00/20.75 **t.** ⓛ 3.95.

X **L'Aventure,** 3 Blenheim Terr., NW8 0EH, ℰ 624 6232, French rest.   p. 20 FS **s**

X **Langan's Bistro,** 26 Devonshire St., W1N 1RJ, ℰ 935 4531   p. 21 IU **e**

X **Nakamura,** 31 Marylebone Lane, W1M 5FH, ℰ 935 2931, Japanese rest. – 🔼 🕮 ⓪ 𝘝𝘐𝘚𝘈   BJ **i**
closed Sunday lunch, Saturday and Bank Holidays – **M** 11.20/36.00 **t.** and a la carte.

X **Chaopraya,** 22 St. Christopher's Pl., W1M 5HD, ℰ 486 0777, Thai rest. – 🔼 🕮 ⓪ 𝘝𝘐𝘚𝘈   BJ **o**
closed Saturday lunch, Sunday and Bank Holidays – **M** 17.00 **t.** and a la carte ⓛ 4.40.

X Taxin Thai Too, 103 Boundary Rd, NW8 0RG, ℰ 372 5497, Thai rest.   FS **a**

X **Sang Thai,** 12-14 Glentworth St., NW1 5PG, ℰ 935 4220, Thai rest. – 🔼 🕮 ⓪ 𝘝𝘐𝘚𝘈   p. 21 HU **a**
closed Saturday and Sunday lunch and Bank Holidays – **M** 12.95 **t.** and a la carte ⓛ 5.95.

X **Il Barbino,** 64 Seymour St., W1H 5AF, ℰ 402 6866, Italian rest. – 🔼 🕮 ⓪ 𝘝𝘐𝘚𝘈   p. 33 EZ **r**
closed Saturday lunch, Sunday and Bank Holidays – **M** a la carte 16.30/20.90 **t.** ⓛ 3.70.

St. James's – ⊠ W1/SW1/WC2 – ☎ 071 – pp. 28 and 29.

🏨 **Ritz,** Piccadilly, W1V 9DG, ℰ 493 8181, Telex 267200, Fax 493 2687, « Elegant restaurant in Louis XV style » – 🛗 ▤ 🆃🆅 ☎. 🔼 🕮 ⓪ 𝘝𝘐𝘚𝘈. ⌘   DN **a**
M 26.50/35.00 **st.** and a la carte 32.00/40.00 **st.** ⓛ 7.00 – ☲ 13.50 – **115 rm** 190.00/265.00 **st.**, **14 suites** 505.00/640.00 **st.**

🏨 **Dukes** ⑤, 35 St. James's Pl., SW1A 1NY, ℰ 491 4840, Telex 28283, Fax 493 1264 – 🛗 ▤ rest 🆃🆅 ☎ – 🔬 30. 🔼 🕮 ⓪ 𝘝𝘐𝘚𝘈. ⌘   EP **x**
M *(closed Saturday lunch)* 19.95/28.50 **t.** and a la carte 29.35/60.40 **t.** – ☲ 11.75 – **36 rm** 180.00/215.00 **t.**, **26 suites** 420.00 **t.**

🏨 **22 Jermyn St.,** 22 Jermyn St., SW1Y 6HL, ℰ 734 2353, Fax 734 0750 – 🛗 🆃🆅 ☎. 🔼 🕮 ⓪ 𝘝𝘐𝘚𝘈. ⌘   FM **e**
M (room service only) a la carte 18.50/23.50 **t.** ⓛ 5.50 – ☲ 10.50 – **5 rm** 165.00/... **13 suites** 230.00/275.00 **st.**

🏨 **Stafford** ⑤, 16-18 St. James's Pl., SW1A 1NJ, ℰ 493 0111, Telex 28602, Fax 493 7121 – 🛗 ▤ rest 🆃🆅 ☎ – 🔬 40   DN **u**
56 rm, **6 suites.**

🏨 **Forte Crest,** 81 Jermyn St., SW1Y 6JF, ℰ 930 2111, Fax 839 2125 – 🛗 🔄 rm ▤ rest 🆃🆅 ☎ ⓟ – 🔬 90. 🔼 🕮 ⓪ 𝘝𝘐𝘚𝘈   EN **i**
M a la carte 22.50/40.00 **st.** – ☲ 8.50 – **255 rm** 135.00/160.00 **st.** – SB (weekends only) 118.00 **st.**

🏨 **Hospitality Inn Piccadilly** (Mt. Charlotte Thistle), 31-39 Coventry St., W1V 8EL, ℰ 930 4033, Telex 8950058, Fax 925 2586 – 🛗 🔄 rm 🆃🆅 ☎. 🔼 🕮 ⓪ 𝘝𝘐𝘚𝘈. ⌘   FGM **a**
M (room service only) – **92 rm** 107.00/120.00 **st.**

🏨 **Royal Trafalgar Thistle** (Mt. Charlotte Thistle), Whitcomb St., WC2H 7HG, ℰ 930 4477, Telex 298564, Fax 925 2149 – 🛗 🔄 rm 🆃🆅 ☎. 🔼 🕮 ⓪ 𝘝𝘐𝘚𝘈. ⌘   GM **r**
M 15.75 **st.** and a la carte ⓛ 5.75 – ☲ 9.75 – **108 rm** 94.00/123.00 **st.**

🏨 **Pastoria,** 3-6 St. Martin's St., WC2H 7HL, ℰ 930 8641, Telex 25538, Fax 925 0551 – 🛗 🆃🆅 ☎ – 🔬 50. 🔼 🕮 ⓪ 𝘝𝘐𝘚𝘈. ⌘   GM **v**
M *(closed Sunday)* a la carte 19.00/25.35 **st.** – ☲ 9.00 – **58 rm** 99.00/119.00 **st.**

X ✿ **Suntory,** 72-73 St. James's St., SW1A 1PH, ℰ 409 0201, Fax 499 7993, Japanese rest. – ▤. 🔼 🕮 ⓪ 𝘝𝘐𝘚𝘈   EP **z**
closed Sunday, New Year and Bank Holidays – **M** 22.00/64.00 **st.** and a la carte 30.80/51.50 **st.** ⓛ 7.00
Spec. Teppan-Yaki, Shabu-Shabu, Sashimi.

XX **Le Caprice,** Arlington House, Arlington St., SW1A 1RT, ℰ 629 2239, Fax 493 9040 –
🖪 🗚🗉 🔘 𝘝𝘐𝘚𝘈
DN
closed 24 December-1 January – **M** a la carte 17.50/32.50 **t.** ⏶ 5.75.

XX **Green's,** 36 Duke St., St. James's, SW1Y 6DF, ℰ 930 4566, Fax 930 1383, English res↑
▤. 🖪 🗚🗉 🔘 𝘝𝘐𝘚𝘈
EN
closed Sunday dinner, Christmas, New Year and Bank Holidays – **M** a la carte 16.25/46.5↑

Soho – ⊠ W1/WC2 – ☎ 071 – pp. 28 and 29.

🏨 **Hampshire** (Edwardian), Leicester Sq., WC2H 7LH, ℰ 839 9399, Telex 9148↑
Fax 930 8122 – ⏸▤ ▤ 📺 ☎ – 🔏 80. 🖪 🗚🗉 🔘 𝘝𝘐𝘚𝘈. ⌘
GM
M 17.50/24.00 **st.** and a la carte ⏶ 6.00 – ⌷ 13.00 – **118 rm** 198.00/237.00 **st.. 5 sui↑**
270.00/648.00 **st.**

🏠 **Hazlitt's** without rest., 6 Frith St., W1V 5TZ, ℰ 434 1771, Fax 439 1524 – 📺 ☎. 🖪 🗚🗉
𝘝𝘐𝘚𝘈. ⌘ – *closed Christmas* – ⌷ 6.00 – **22 rm** 95.00/105.00 **s.**, **1 suite** 150.00 **s.**
FK

XXX **Lindsay House,** 21 Romilly St., WIV 5TG, ℰ 439 0450, Fax 581 2848 – ▤. 🖪 🗚🗉 🔘 𝘝𝘐↑
closed 25 and 26 December – **M** 14.75 **t.** (lunch) and a la carte 29.50/34.40 **t.** ⏶ 4.50. GL

XXX **Au Jardin des Gourmets,** 5 Greek St., W1V 5LA, ℰ 437 1816, Fax 437 0043, Fren↑
rest. – ▤. 🖪 🗚🗉 🔘 𝘝𝘐𝘚𝘈
GJ
closed Saturday lunch, Sunday, Easter, Christmas and Bank Holidays – **M** (booking ess↑
tial) 17.95/18.50 **t.** and a la carte ⏶ 3.75.

XXX **Red Fort,** 77 Dean St., W1V 5HA, ℰ 437 2525, Indian rest. – 🖪 🗚🗉 🔘 𝘝𝘐𝘚𝘈 FJK
closed Christmas Day – **M** a la carte 15.90/25.20 **st.**

XXX **La Bastide,** 50 Greek St., W1V 5LQ, ℰ 734 3300, French rest. – 🖪 🗚🗉 🔘 𝘝𝘐𝘚𝘈
closed Saturday lunch, Sunday, Christmas-New Year and Bank Holidays – **M** 23.0↑
(lunch) and a la carte 24.70/30.90 **t.** ⏶ 7.00.
GK

XX ✿ **Sutherlands,** 45 Lexington St., W1R 3LG, ℰ 434 3401, Fax 287 2997 – ▤. 🖪 🗚🗉 𝘝𝘐𝘚𝘈
closed Saturday lunch, Sunday and Bank Holidays – **M** 24.00/39.50 **t.** ⏶ 5.75
EK
Spec. Terrine of scallops, oysters and leeks with a Chardonnay and saffron stock, Baked sea bass with braised en↑
and a dark fennel sauce, Tournedos of beef wrapped in Parma ham with a rich thyme sauce.

XX **L'Escargot,** 48 Greek St., W1V 5LQ, ℰ 437 2679, Fax 437 0790, French rest. – ▤. 🖪
🔘 𝘝𝘐𝘚𝘈
GK
closed Saturday lunch, Sunday, Easter, Christmas and Bank Holidays – **M** (booking ess↑
tial) 12.50 **t.** (dinner) and a la carte 15.25/24.00 **t.** ⏶ 4.40.

XX **L'Hippocampe,** 63 Frith St., W1V 5TA, ℰ 734 4545, French Seafood rest. – ▤. 🖪 🗚🗉
𝘝𝘐𝘚𝘈
FK
closed Saturday lunch, Sunday, Easter, Christmas-New Year and Bank Holiday Saturday
M 16.50 **t.** and a la carte ⏶ 4.75.

XX **Ming,** 35-36 Greek St., W1V 5LN, ℰ 734 2721, Chinese rest. – 🖪 🗚🗉 🔘 𝘝𝘐𝘚𝘈 GK
closed Sunday and 25-26 December – **M** 13.00/19.00 **t.** and a la carte ⏶ 6.00.

XX **Gopal's,** 12 Bateman St., W1V 5TD, ℰ 434 0840, Indian rest. – ▤. 🖪 🗚🗉 🔘 𝘝𝘐𝘚𝘈
M 10.50/15.00 **t.** and a la carte ⏶ 3.25.
GK

XX **Kaya,** 22-25 Dean St., W1V 5AL, ℰ 437 6630, Korean rest. – ▤ FJ

XX **Gay Hussar,** 2 Greek St., W1V 6NB, ℰ 437 0973, Hungarian rest. – ▤. 🗚🗉 GJ
closed Sunday – **M** 15.00 **t.** (lunch) and a la carte 16.20/23.50 **st.** ⏶ 3.00.

XX **Gallery Rendezvous,** 53-55 Beak St., W1R 3LF, ℰ 734 0445, Chinese (Peking) res↑
▤. 🖪 🗚🗉 🔘 𝘝𝘐𝘚𝘈 – **M** 12.50/38.00 **t.** and a la carte ⏶ 5.00.
EL

X **Sri Siam,** 14 Old Compton St., W1V 5PE, ℰ 434 3544, Thai rest. – ▤. 🖪 🗚🗉 🔘 𝘝𝘐𝘚𝘈
closed Sunday lunch, 24 to 26 December and 1 January – **M** 9.50/15.50 **t.** and a la ca↑
⏶ 3.95.
GK

X **Alastair Little,** 49 Frith St., W1V 5TE, ℰ 734 5183 – 🖪 𝘝𝘐𝘚𝘈
FK
closed Saturday lunch, Sunday and Bank Holidays – **M** 23.00 **t.** (lunch) and a la carte 28.↑
39.00 **t.**

X **Frith's,** 14 Frith St., W1V 5TS, ℰ 439 3370 – ⏛. 🖪 𝘝𝘐𝘚𝘈
FGK
closed Saturday lunch, Sunday, Easter, Christmas and Bank Holidays – **M** a la carte 20.↑
32.50 **st.**

X **Fung Shing,** 15 Lisle St., WC2H 7BE, ℰ 437 1539, Chinese (Canton) rest. – 🖪 🗚🗉 🔘
M 11.00/12.00 **t.** and a la carte.
GL

X **Van Long,** 40 Frith St., W1V 5HL, ℰ 439 1835, Vietnamese rest. GK

X **Saigon,** 45 Frith St., W1V 5TE, ℰ 437 7109, Vietnamese rest. – 🖪 🗚🗉 🔘 𝘝𝘐𝘚𝘈 FGK
closed Sunday and Bank Holidays – **M** 14.40/17.40 **t.** and a la carte.

Strand and Covent Garden – ⊠ WC2 – ☎ 071 – Except where otherwise stated s↑
p. 33.

🏨 **Savoy,** Strand, WC2R 0EU, ℰ 836 4343, Telex 24234, Fax 240 6040 – ⏸▤ ⏛ rm ▤ 📺
⟐ – 🔏 450. 🖪 🗚🗉 🔘 𝘝𝘐𝘚𝘈. ⌘
DEY
M Grill (*closed Saturday lunch, Sunday, 5 and 31 August and Bank Holidays*) 29.7↑
(dinner) and a la carte 29.60/41.45 **t.** ⏶ 5.35 – **River** 24.95/38.50 **st.** and a la carte 35.↑
45.10 **st.** ⏶ 5.35 – ⌷ 15.75 – **150 rm** 180.00/275.00 **st.**, **50 suites** 300.00/650.00 **s**
SB (weekends only) 310.00/530.00 **st.**

Howard, 12 Temple Pl., WC2R 2PR, ℰ 836 3555, Telex 268047, Fax 379 4547 – ▯ ▤ 📺
☎ ⇔ – 🛦 100. 🔼 AE ① VISA ⋘
EX **e**
M 15.00/25.00 **st.** and a la carte ᠗ 4.50 – ☷ 13.85 – **133 rm** 200.00/226.00 **st., 2 suites**
270.00/465.00 **st.**

Waldorf (Forte), Aldwych, WC2B 4DD, ℰ 836 2400, Telex 24574, Fax 836 7244 – ▯
⋘← rm 📺 ☎ – 🛦 400. 🔼 AE ① VISA ⋘
EX **x**
M 15.50/18.00 **st.** and a la carte ᠗ 7.95 – ☷ 11.00 – **291 rm** 125.00/155.00 **st., 19 suites**
240.00/425.00 **st.** – SB (weekends only) 108.00/278.00 **st.**

Boulestin, 1a Henrietta St., WC2E 8PS, ℰ 836 7061, Fax 836 1283, French rest. – ▤. 🔼
AE ① VISA
DX **r**
closed Saturday lunch, Sunday, last 2 weeks August and Bank Holidays – M 18.75 **st.**
(lunch) and a la carte ᠗ 6.50.

Now and Zen, 4a Upper St. Martin's Lane, WC2H 9EA, ℰ 497 0376, Chinese rest. – ▤.
🔼 AE ① VISA
DX **x**
closed 3 days at Christmas – M a la carte 25.30/50.30 **t.**

Simpson's-in-the-Strand, 100 Strand, WC2R 0EW, ℰ 836 9112, Fax 836 1381, English
rest. – ▤. 🔼 AE ① VISA ⋘
EX **o**
closed Sunday and Bank Holidays – M (booking essential) 18.50 **t.** and a la carte ᠗ 4.95.

Ivy, 1 West St., WC2H 9NE, ℰ 836 4751, Fax 497 3644 – ▤. 🔼 AE ① VISA
GK **z**
closed 25 and 26 December – M a la carte 19.00/32.25 **t.** ᠗ 5.75.

Orso, 27 Wellington St., WC2E 7DA, ℰ 240 5269, Fax 497 2148, Italian rest. – ▤ EX **z**
closed 25 and 26 December – M (booking essential) a la carte 19.00/23.50 **t.** ᠗ 5.00.

Gritti, 11 Upper St. Martin's Lane, WC2, ℰ 836 5121, Italian rest. – ▤. 🔼 AE ① VISA
DX **e**
closed Sunday and Bank Holidays – M 14.75/20.75 **t.** and a la carte ᠗ 8.50.

Sheekey's, 28-32 St. Martin's Court, WC2N 4AL, ℰ 240 2565, Seafood – ▤. 🔼 AE ①
VISA
DX **v**
closed Saturday lunch, Sunday and Bank Holidays – M 19.00/25.00 **t.** and a la carte ᠗ 4.50.

Magno's Brasserie, 65a Long Acre, WC2E 9JH, ℰ 836 6077, French rest. – ▤. 🔼 AE ①
VISA
DV **e**
closed Saturday lunch, Sunday, Christmas-New Year and Bank Holidays – M 9.45 **st.**
(dinner) and a la carte 15.35/21.75 **t.** ᠗ 5.95.

Laguna, 50 St. Martin's Lane, WC2N 4EA, ℰ 836 0960, Italian rest. – ▤ DX **z**

Victoria – ⊠ SW1 – ✆ 071 – Except where otherwise stated see p. 32.
🛈 Victoria Station Forecourt ℰ 730 3488.

St. James Court, Buckingham Gate, SW1E 6AF, ℰ 834 6655, Telex 938075,
Fax 630 7587, 🔥, ⇌ – ▯ ⋘← rm ▤ rest 📺 ☎ – 🛦 180. 🔼 AE ① VISA ⋘
CX **i**
M (see **Auberge de Provence** and **Inn of Happiness** below) – ☷ 12.50 – **363 rm** 150.00/
190.00 **s.. 27 suites** 250.00/700.00 **s.**

Royal Horseguards Thistle (Mt. Charlotte Thistle), 2 Whitehall Court, SW1A 2EJ,
ℰ 839 3400, Telex 917096, Fax 925 2263 – ▯ ⋘← rm ▤ rest 📺 ☎ – 🛦 60. 🔼 AE ① VISA ⋘
M (closed Saturday, Sunday and Bank Holidays) 17.50/22.45 **st.** and a la carte ᠗ 7.50 –
☷ 10.25 – **368 rm** 99.00/110.00 **st., 8 suites** 385.00 **st.**
p. 26 LX **a**

Stakis St. Ermin's, 2 Caxton St., SW1H 0QW, ℰ 222 7888, Telex 917731, Fax 222 6914
– ▯ ⋘← rm ▤ rest 📺 ☎ – 🛦 150. 🔼 AE ① VISA ⋘
CX **a**
M (carving rest.) 15.00/17.50 **st.** and a la carte ᠗ 5.95 – ☷ 9.75 – **282 rm** 127.60/161.70 **st.,**
8 suites 295.00 **st.** – SB (weekends only) 92.00/104.00 **st.**

Goring, 15 Beeston Pl., Grosvenor Gdns., SW1W 0JW, ℰ 834 8211, Telex 919166,
Fax 834 4393 – ▯ 📺 ☎ – 🛦 50. 🔼 AE ① VISA ⋘
BX **a**
M 19.50/23.00 **t.** and a la carte ᠗ 6.50 – ☷ 10.50 – **80 rm** 120.00/175.00 **st., 4 suites**
205.00 **st.**

Royal Westminster Thistle (Mt. Charlotte Thistle), 49 Buckingham Palace Rd, SW1W 0QT,
ℰ 834 1821, Telex 916821, Fax 931 7542 – ▯ ⋘← rm ▤ rest 📺 ☎ – 🛦 150. 🔼 AE ① VISA ⋘
☷ 9.95 – **134 rm** 118.00/180.00 **st.**
BX **z**

Grosvenor (Mt. Charlotte Thistle), 101 Buckingham Palace Rd, SW1W 0SJ, ℰ 834 9494,
Telex 916006, Fax 630 1978 – ▯ ⋘← rm ▤ rest 📺 ☎ – 🛦 150. 🔼 AE ① VISA ⋘
BX **e**
M (carving rest.) 15.35 **st.** and a la carte ᠗ 4.80 – ☷ 8.75 – **363 rm** 98.00/190.00 **st., 3 suites**
245.00/325.00 **st.**

Rubens, 39-41 Buckingham Palace Rd, SW1W 0PS, ℰ 834 6600, Telex 916577,
Fax 828 5401 – ▯ ⋘← rm ▤ rest 📺 ☎ – 🛦 60. 🔼 AE ① VISA ⋘
BX **n**
M (buffet lunch Saturday and Sunday) 14.20/15.75 **st.** and a la carte – ☷ 9.40 – **189 rm**
97.00/215.00 **st.**

Scandic Crown, 2 Bridge Pl., SW1V 1QA, ℰ 834 8123, Telex 914973, Fax 828 1099, 🔥,
⇌, ▦ – ▯ ⋘← rm ▤ 📺 ☎ – 🛦 200. 🔼 AE ① VISA ⋘
BY **i**
M 16.75 **st.** (lunch) and a la carte 14.75/23.70 **st.** ᠗ 5.00 – ☷ 8.50 – **205 rm** 107.00/
137.50 **st.. 5 suites** 219.50 **st.**

Ebury Court, 26 Ebury St., SW1W 0LU, ℰ 730 8147, Fax 823 5966 – ▯ 📺 ☎. 🔼 AE ①
VISA
AX **i**
closed 2 weeks Christmas-New Year – M (closed Saturday lunch) 16.50 **t.** ᠗ 4.00 – **45 rm**
☷ 70.00/150.00 **t.**

🏠 **Hamilton House,** 60-64 Warwick Way, SW1V 1SA, ℰ 821 7113, Fax 630 0806 – 📺 ☎
VISA. 🕸
40 rm.
Bʸ

🏠 **Winchester** without rest., 17 Belgrave Rd, SW1V 1RB, ℰ 828 2972, Telex 269
Fax 828 5191 – 📺
18 rm.
Bʸ

↑ **Harcourt House** without rest., 50 Ebury St., SW1W 0LU, ℰ 730 2722 – 📺. **AE VISA**.
closed 23 December-3 January – **9 rm** � 36.00/55.00 **st.**
Aʸ

↑ **Collin House** without rest., 104 Ebury St., SW1W 9QD, ℰ 730 8031 – 🕸
closed 2 weeks Christmas – **13 rm** � 34.00/54.00 **t.**
Aʸ

XXX **Inn of Happiness** (at St. James Court H.), Buckingham Gate, SW1E 6AF, ℰ 821 1
Telex 938075, Fax 630 7587, Chinese rest. – ▤. **AE ⓪ VISA**
closed lunch Saturday and Bank Holidays – **M** 20.00/30.00 **t.** and a la carte.
C

XXX **Auberge de Provence** (at St. James Court H.), Buckingham Gate, SW1E █
ℰ 821 1899, Telex 938075, Fax 630 7587, French rest. – ▤. **AE ⓪ VISA**
closed Saturday lunch, Sunday and Bank Holidays – **M** 25.00/30.00 **t.** and a la carte 🅰 5
C

XXX **Santini,** 29 Ebury St., SW1W 0NZ, ℰ 730 4094, Fax 730 0544, Italian rest. – ▤. **AE**
VISA
closed Saturday and Sunday lunch and Bank Holidays – **M** 18.25 **t.** (lunch) and
carte 24.60/52.25 **t.**
AB

XXX **L'Incontro,** 87 Pimlico Rd, SW1W 8PH, ℰ 730 6327, Fax 730 5062, Italian rest. – ▤
AE ⓪ VISA p. 31 F
closed Sunday and Bank Holidays – **M** 18.25 **t.** (lunch) and a la carte 23.55/45.6

XX **Green's,** Marsham Court, Marsham St., SW1P 4JY, ℰ 834 9552, English rest. – ▤.
⓪ VISA p. 26 L
closed Sunday lunch, Saturday and Bank Holidays – **M** (booking essential) a la carte 17
79.50 **t.**

XX **Ken Lo's Memories of China,** 67-69 Ebury St., SW1W 0NZ, ℰ 730 7734, Chinese r
– ▤. **AE ⓪ VISA**
closed Sunday and Bank Holidays – **M** 20.00/40.00 **t.** and a la carte.
Aʸ

XX **Ciboure,** 21 Eccleston St., SW1W 9LX, ℰ 730 2505, French rest. – ▤. **AE**
VISA
closed Saturday lunch, Sunday dinner and 2 August-2 September – **M** 13.00/15.00 **t.**
Aʸ

XX **Simply Nico,** 48a Rochester Row, SW1P 1JU, ℰ 630 8061 – **AE ⓪ VISA**
*closed lunch Saturday and Bank Holidays, Sunday, 4 days at Easter, and 10 day
Christmas* – **M** (booking essential) 27.00/29.00 **st.**
Cʸ

XX **Kym's,** 70-71 Wilton Rd, SW1V 1DE, ℰ 828 8931, Chinese (Szechuan, Hunan) rest. –
AE VISA
M 7.50/12.50 **t.** and a la carte 🅰 4.00.
Bʸ

XX **Hunan,** 51 Pimlico Rd, SW1W 8NE, ℰ 730 5712, Chinese (Hunan) rest. – **AE VISA**
M 10.00/18.50 **t.** and a la carte 🅰 4.00. p. 25 I2

XX **Eatons,** 49 Elizabeth St., SW1W 9PP, ℰ 730 0074 – **AE ⓪ VISA**
closed Saturday, Sunday and Bank Holidays – **M** 11.80 **s.** and a la carte 🅰 4.40.
Aʸ

XX **L'Amico,** 44 Horseferry Rd, SW1P 2AF, ℰ 222 4680, Italian rest. – **AE**
VISA p. 26 Lʸ
closed Saturday and Sunday – **M** (booking essential) a la carte 18.00/32.60 **st.** 🅰 4.40.

XX **Gran Paradiso,** 52 Wilton Rd, SW1V 1DE, ℰ 828 5818, Italian rest. – **AE ⓪ VISA**
closed Saturday lunch, Sunday, last 2 weeks August and Bank Holidays – **M** and a
carte 16.00/20.80 **t.** 🅰 3.00.
Bʸ

X **Tate Gallery,** Tate Gallery, Millbank, SW1P 4RG, ℰ 834 6754, English rest., « █
Whistler murals » – ▤. **AE VISA** p. 26 L2
closed Sunday, 17 April, 1 May, 24 to 26 December and 1 January – **M** (lunch o
(booking essential) a la carte 16.80/22.20 **t.** 🅰 5.40.

X **La Poule au Pot,** 231 Ebury St., SW1W 8UT, ℰ 730 7763, French rest. – **AE ⓪**
closed Saturday lunch and Sunday – **M** 12.25/25.00 **st.** and a la carte. p. 25 I2

X **Mimmo d'Ischia,** 61 Elizabeth St., SW1W 9PP, ℰ 730 5406, Italian rest. – **AE ⓪**
closed Sunday and Bank Holidays – **M** 25.00/50.00 **t.** and a la carte 🅰 6.50.
Aʸ

X **La Fontana,** 101 Pimlico Rd, SW1W 8PH, ℰ 730 6630, Italian rest. – **AE ⓪ VISA**
closed Bank Holidays – **M** a la carte 24.00/32.00 **t.** 🅰 5.80. p. 31 F

X **Villa Medici,** 35 Belgrave Rd, SW1 5AX, ℰ 828 3613, Italian rest. – **AE**
VISA
Bʸ
closed Saturday lunch, Sunday and Bank Holidays – **M** a la carte 16.30/20.50 **t.** 🅰 3.70

When in a hurry use the Michelin Main Road Maps:
970 *Europe,* **980** *Greece,* **984** *Germany,* **985** *Scandinavia-Finland,*
986 *Great Britain and Ireland,* **987** *Germany-Austria-Benelux,* **988** *Italy,*
989 *France,* **990** *Spain-Portugal and* **991** *Yugoslavia.*

Car manufacturers' adresses
Adresses des marques automobiles
Indirizzi delle marche automobilistiche
Adressen der Automobilfirmen

Romeo (GB) Ltd
Poulton Close   Dover   Kent CT17 OHP
Tél.: (0304) 212500

on Martin Lagonda Ltd
Tickford Street   Newport Pagnell
Bucks MK16 9AN
Tél.: (0908) 610620

W (GB) Ltd
Ellesfield Avenue   Bracknell
Breks RG12 4TA   Tél. (0344) 426565

oën UK Ltd
221 Bath Road   Slough   Berks
SL1 4BA   Tél, (0753) 812100

t Mitsubishi
Colt Car Co. Ltd   Watermore
Cirencester   Glos GL7 1LS
Tél.: (0285) 655777

Auto (UK) Ltd
Fiat House   266 Bath Road   Slough
Berks SL1 4HJ   Tél.: (0753) 511431

d Motor Company Ltd
Eagle Way   Brentwood   Essex CM13
3BW   Tél.: (0277) 253000

Cars Ltd
77 Mount Ephraim   Turnbridge TN4
8BS   Tél.: (0892) 511811

da (UK) Ltd
Power Road   Chiswick   London W4
5YT   Tél.: 081-747 1400

ndal Car Distributors (UK) Ltd
Ryder Street   West Bromwich
West Midlands B70 OEJ
Tél.: 021-522 2000

u (UK) Ltd
Ryder Street   West Bromwich
West Midlands B70 OEJ
Tél.: 021-522 2000

uar Cars Ltd
Allesley   Coventry
West Midlands CV5 9DR
Tél.: (0203) 402121

a Cars
Western House   Middle Lane   Wythall
Birmingham   West Midlands B47 6LA
Tél.: (0753) 690690

cia UK Concessionaries
266 Bath Road   Slough   Berk
SL1 4HJ   Tél.: (0753) 690690

Land Rover Lt
Lode Lane   Solihull   West Midlands
B92 8NW   Tél.: 021-722 2424

Leyland Daf
Cornwall Street   Birmingham
West Midlands B3 2DG
Tél.: 021-233 0011

Lotus Group
Hethel   Norwich   Norfolk NR14 8EZ
Tél.: (0953) 608000

Mazda Cars (UK) Ltd
77 Mount Ephraim   Tunbridge Wells
Kent TN4 8BS   Tél.: (0892) 511877

Mercedes Benz (UK) Ltd
Delaware Drive   Tongwell
Milton Keynes MK15 8BA
Tél.: (0908) 668899

Nissan (UK) Ltd
Nissan House   Columbia Drive
Worthing
West Sussex BN13 68561

Peugeot Talbot
Motor Compagny Ltd   Aldermoor
House   PO Box 227   Aldermoor Lane
Coventry
West Midlands CV3 1LT
Tél.: (0203) 884000

Porsche Cars (GB) Ltd
Bath Road   Calcot, Reading   Berks
RG3 7SE   Tél.: (0734) 303666

Proton Cars (UK) Ltd
Western House   Middle Lane   Wythall
Birmingham   West Midlands
B47 6LA
Tél.: (0564) 826167

Renault (UK) Ltd
Western Avenue   London W3 ORZ
Tél.: 081-992 3481

Rolls-Royce Motors Cars Ltd
Pyms Lane   Crewe   Cheshire CW1
3PL
Tél.: (0203) 255155

Rover Group Ltd
Canley Road   Coventry   West Mid-
lands CV5 6QX
Tél.: (0203) 670111

Saab (GB) Ltd
Saab House   Globe Park   Marlow
Bucks SL7 1LY   Tél.: (0628) 486977

Seat Concessionaries (UK) Ltd
Seat House Gatwixk Road
Crawley West Sussex RH10 2AX
Tél.: (0293) 514141

Skoda (GB) Ltd
150 Goswell Road London
EC1V 7DS Tél.: 071-253 7441

Súbaru (UK) Ltd
Ryder Street West Bromwich
West Midlands B70 OEJ
Tél.: 021-522 2000

Heron-Suzuki GB Cars
40-46 Gatwick Road Crawley West
Sussex RH10 2XF
Tél.: (0293) 518000

Toyota (GB) Ltd
The Quadrangle Redhill
Surrey RH1 1PX
Tél.: (0737) 768585

VAG (UK) Ltd
Yeomans Drive Blakelands Milton
Keynes MK14 5AN
Tél.: (0908) 679121

Vauxhall Motors Ltd
Griffin House PO Box 3 Osborne
Road
Luton Beds LU1 3YT
Tél.: (0582) 21122

Volvo Concessionaries Ltd
Globe Park Marlow Bucks
SL7 1YQ
Tél.: (0628) 477977

Yugo Cars
Worcester House Basingstoke Roa
Reading
Berks RG2 0QB
Tél.: (0734) 866921

MANUFACTURE FRANÇAISE DES PNEUMATIQUES MICHELIN

Société en commandite par actions au capital de 2 000 000 000 de francs

Place des Carmes-Déchaux – 63 Clermont-Ferrand (France)

R.C.S. Clermont-Fd B 855 200 507

© Michelin et Cie, Propriétaires-Éditeurs 1992

Dépôt légal 2-92 – ISBN 2-06-006629-8

Printed in France : 12-91-25

Photocomposition : APS, Tours – Impression : TARDY-QUERCY, Bourges

**Great Britain
and Ireland**
hotels and
restaurants

986
Great Britain
Ireland
Grande-Bretagne
Irlande

1 in. 16 miles – 1/1 000 000

MICHELIN

MICHELIN
GREAT BRITAIN
and IRELAND

**Great Britain
and Ireland**

GREEN TOURIST GUIDES

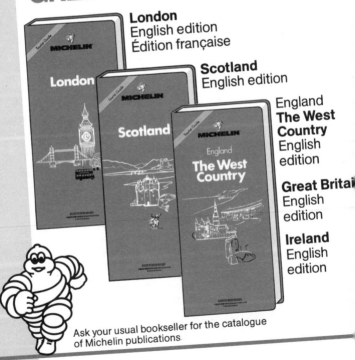

London
English edition
Édition française

Scotland
English edition

England
**The West
Country**
English
edition

Great Britai
English
edition

Ireland
English
edition

Ask your usual bookseller for the catalogue
of Michelin publications.